**5/13**

1078

# Holes, g
# and cav
# Stages 1

C000141382

A Unit for teachers

Published for the Schools Council by
Macdonald Educational, London and New York

© Schools Council Publications 1973

First impression 1973
Second impression (with amendments) 1974
Third impression (with amendments) 1976

ISBN 0 356 04108 5

Published by
**Macdonald Educational**
Holywell House
Worship Street
London EC2

850 Seventh Avenue
New York 10019

The chief author of this book is:

Roy Richards

The other members of the Science 5/13 team are:

| | |
|---|---|
| Len Ennever | Project Director |
| Albert James | Deputy Project Director |
| Wynne Harlen | Evaluator |
| Sheila Parker | |
| Don Radford | |
| Mary Horn | |

Made and printed by Waterlow (Dunstable) Limited

# General preface

'Science 5/13' is a project sponsored jointly by the Schools Council, the Nuffield Foundation and the Scottish Education Department, and based at the University of Bristol School of Education. It aims at helping teachers to help children between the ages of five and thirteen years to learn science through first-hand experience using a variety of methods.

The Project produces books that comprise Units dealing with subject areas in which children are likely to conduct investigations. Some of these Units are supported by books of background information. The Units are linked by objectives that the Project team hopes children will attain through their work. The aims of the Project are explained in a general guide for teachers called *With objectives in mind* which contains the Project's guide to Objectives for children learning science, reprinted at the back of each Unit.

## Acknowledgements

## Metrication

The Project is deeply grateful to its many friends: to the local education authorities who have helped us work in their areas, to those of their staff who, acting as area representatives, have borne the heavy brunt of administering our trials, and to the teachers, heads and wardens who have been generous without stint in working with their children on our materials. The books we have written drew substance from the work they did for us, and it was through their critical appraisal that our materials reached their present form. For guidance, we had our sponsors, our Consultative Committee and, for support, in all our working, the University of Bristol. To all of them we acknowledge our many debts: their help has been invaluable.

This has given us a great deal to think about. We have been given much good advice by well-informed friends, and we have consulted many reports by learned bodies. Following the advice and the reports wherever possible we have expressed quantities in metric units with Imperial units afterwards in square brackets if it seemed useful to state them so.

There are, however, some cases to which the recommendations are difficult to apply. For instance we have difficulty with units such as miles per hour (which has statutory force in this country) and with some Imperial units that are still in current use for common commodities and, as far as we know, liable to remain so for some time. In these cases we have tried to use our common sense, and, in order to make statements that are both accurate and helpful to teachers we have quoted Imperial measures followed by the approximate metric equivalents in square brackets if it seemed sensible to give them.

Where we have quoted statements made by children, or given illustrations that are children's work, we have left unaltered the units in which the children worked — in any case some of these units were arbitrary.

# Contents

**Illustration acknowledgements:**

The publishers gratefully acknowledge the help given by the following in supplying photographs on the pages indicated:

Ardea Photographs, 69
British Hovercraft Corporation Limited, 17
Bruce Coleman Limited, Photographer S. C. Bisserot,
71 bottom, Photographer Russ Kinne, 71 top, 77
Fishing News, 65
Haslemere Educational Museum, 76 right
Italian State Tourist Office, 2
L. Hugh Newman's Natural History Photographic
Agency, 68, 76 left, 79, 80
Metropolitan Water Board, 61
Post Office, 13
Radio Times Hulton Picture Library, 48 top
South West Picture Agency Limited, 23, 30, 32, 39
Science Museum, London, 25, 48 bottom, 53
Walter Tilgner, 66
The Wellcome Trustees, 81
Yale Locks, 17

Extract reproduced from the Ordnance Survey Map with the sanction of the Controller of H.M. Stationery Office, Crown Copyright reserved, 38

Line drawings by The Garden Studio: Anna Barnard

Flow charts and labelling by Graeme Wilson Associates

Cover design by Peter Gauld

# Introduction

There are many stimuli constantly bombarding young children which cause them to observe, discover and learn through their own experience. It is characteristic of such children that they acquire knowledge, skills and methods of learning in a seemingly haphazard way, often butterflying from one topic or activity to another. They delight in collecting things, finding out, experimenting, watching, wondering and communicating their discoveries to others. Working as individuals or in small groups or sometimes as a class they discuss problems, decide how to tackle them and go about their separate tasks.

*Holes, gaps and cavities* is so written as to take note of these basic traits of children. The first chapter allows for the acquisitive nature of children in that they can make their own collection of 'holes', make lists of holes, look for holes indoors and outdoors and make their own holes. Succeeding chapters are based on doing things that arise out of this first contact with holes.

The Unit is concerned with a number of facets of 'holes, gaps and cavities', all of which lead to a gathering of experience. It is hoped that such facets are capable of extension in many directions and that any group of children working on the Unit will come up with avenues of their own to explore.

Finally, perhaps, will come the realisation that the world of 'holes, gaps and cavities' is vital to us, indeed without it our animate world would soon come to a halt.

## Objectives

What are our objectives in such work? The Project's book *With objectives in mind* discusses and enumerates those objectives that might be suitably pursued and attained with young children. This is not to say that all possible objectives are put forward for there will be many objectives peculiar to a class, or a group or an individual child which will arise only in a given circumstance.

These are, of course, foremost and well worthy of pursuit but it is hoped that the stated objectives in *With objectives in mind* will also prove helpful. Basically these are of two kinds:

i. Those that will help develop attitudes, interests and aesthetic awareness.

ii. Those that will help develop basic concepts, skills and knowledge.

Many objectives will arise from a study of 'holes, gaps and cavities'. Lots like the following will be very general:

*Ability to find simple answers to problems by investigation.*

*Appreciation of the need to control variables and use controls in investigations.*

*Awareness of cause–effect relationships.*

*Awareness of structure–function relationship of parts of living things.*

Whilst others will be more specific to a given activity, for example:

*Recognition of the action of force.*

*Awareness of sources of electricity.*

# Just holes and how to make them

## Starting points

### Make a collection of holes
One of the best ways to start on holes is to collect
some. It is not the number of holes collected that
interests us here but rather that we will begin to look
at holes more closely, question their function and begin
to gather starting points for further study.

There are many 'starting points' in such a collection:

Why does the recorder make high and low notes?

What sort of water timers can we make?
(see *Time*).

Who can make the most efficient sieving mechanism?
(page 54).

A large hole – the crater of the volcano Mount Etna. Where are volcanoes found? Mark them on a map of the world. Do the marks make a pattern?

3

Try taking a household tap to pieces. Look at the working mechanism.

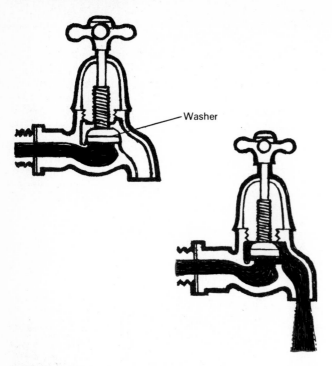

Washer

What other kinds and uses of taps are there?

Can children find out more about the movement of a balloon? (page 17).

Who can make the best hovercraft? (page 17).

What can we find out about bubbles? (page 22).

Make drops of water with the pipette. What can be found out about them? (page 27).

How well do tissues absorb water? (page 60).

Shoot a stream of water from a squeezy bottle. What can be found out about it? (page 34).

Why are there holes and cavities in bones? Make a collection. (page 74).

How well do liquids pass through a cotton handkerchief? What about other fabrics? (page 58).

How does a telephone work?

Do different sponges have different absorption rates?

How many ways can you find of stopping up holes?

## Make a list of holes

Make a long list of all the different kinds of holes you can think of. Try classifying them.

Here is one school's attempt:

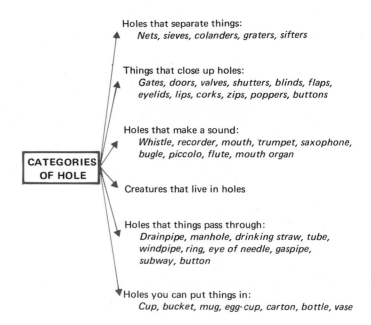

CATEGORIES OF HOLE

Holes that separate things:
    Nets, sieves, colanders, graters, sifters

Things that close up holes:
    Gates, doors, valves, shutters, blinds, flaps,
    eyelids, lips, corks, zips, poppers, buttons

Holes that make a sound:
    Whistle, recorder, mouth, trumpet, saxophone,
    bugle, piccolo, flute, mouth organ

Creatures that live in holes

Holes that things pass through:
    Drainpipe, manhole, drinking straw, tube,
    windpipe, ring, eye of needle, gaspipe,
    subway, button

Holes you can put things in:
    Cup, bucket, mug, egg-cup, carton, bottle, vase

Collect objects to illustrate each category or collect pictures and make up charts to illustrate your classification.

## Make collections of pictures

Try making books or charts using pictures cut from magazines. You might make up collections showing:

Musical instruments worked by air passing through holes.

Tools used to make holes.

Kitchen implements with holes.

Machines used for digging holes.

## Look for holes in the classroom

Where are all the holes in a classroom? Inkwells, power-points, windows, ventilation grilles, keyholes, taps, screw-holes. What about articles in our pockets or clothing, do these have holes? Usually all these holes are for a purpose.

Let us look at a few of these holes as starting points. Where might they lead us?

### Caps

Caps have cavities to fit heads. Carry out a survey through the school and plot a graph of cap size against age.

Is there any correlation?

Would it be possible to predict the cap size of a newcomer to the class?

Other head measurements might be interesting. Measure the distance around the head using string. Pieces of string cut to different head sizes turn into a ready-made histogram. Opticians are interested in the distance between the eye and the ear.

How does it vary in the class?

What about head shapes?

It is said there are two basic sorts. Is this so?

One school investigated shoe sizes as well. Do children with the biggest feet have the biggest heads?

## Keyholes

How many different kinds of keyhole are there in a school? What about at home? Make a class collection of keyhole drawings.

At a simple level a keyhole allows access of a key, which is just a simple lever, to a lock, but how exactly does a lock work? Take the back off an old lock and look at the mechanism. Try and do this carefully so that the bits and pieces making up the interior mechanism still interlock. It is often difficult to put them together once they come apart.

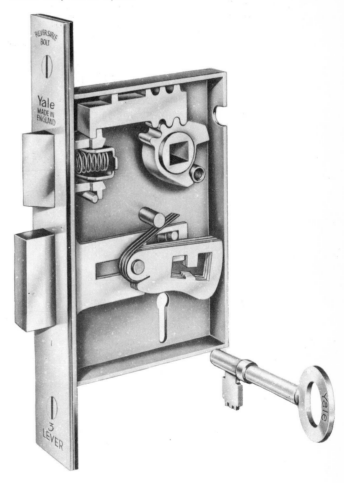

Interior of a lock

5

Try making a collection of locks.

What other devices are there for securing things? The topic of safely securing a house might be an interesting one for discussion.

Where else does man make use of levers?

Try levering up a table using two pieces of timber.

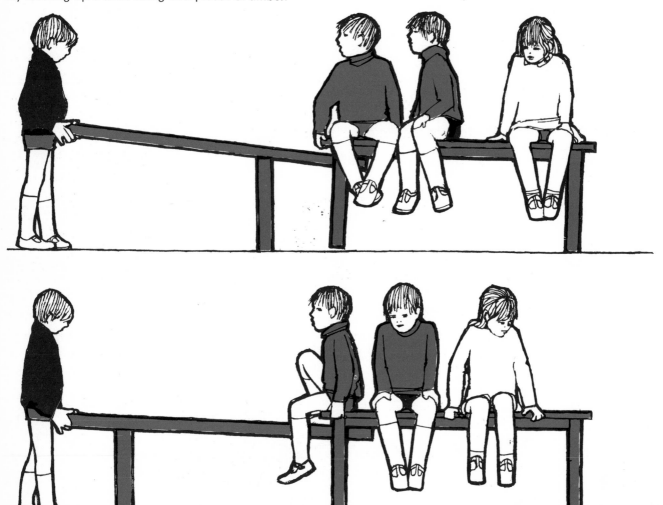

What difference does varying the position of your balancing point (pivot or fulcrum) make?

Try closing a door by pushing it near the hinge end. Then try by pushing near the lock. Which is easier? Why?

Try measuring how effective a lever can be. Lift a block as shown in the diagram.

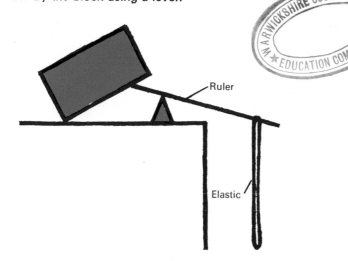

Elastic

Now try the block using a lever.

Ruler

Elastic

How much easier is it to do this with a lever?

Look for examples of places where levers are found. Single ones, as in a sardine tin opener, and double ones as in a pair of scissors or a pair of pliers. Don't forget to look at levers in animals, at joints in ourselves or at the pincers of a crab.

## Power-points

Why are there three holes in an electric socket? This is a question that may well be asked. Care must be exercised because of the physical dangers involved but here lies a lot of worthwhile science because the whole field of electricity is immediately opened up. This is too wide a topic for us to consider here but it is, perhaps, worth mentioning that the third hole is a safety device.

Take a three-pin plug apart and note how it is wired and how there is another safety device, a fuse, present.

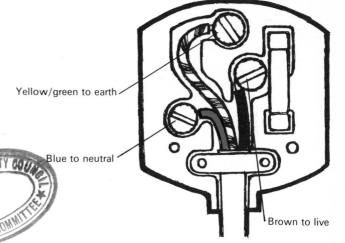

Yellow/green to earth

Blue to neutral

Brown to live

It is easy to demonstrate the function of a fuse.

Put a long thin piece of aluminium foil into an electric circuit. If you experiment and get it about the right length and thickness it should melt.

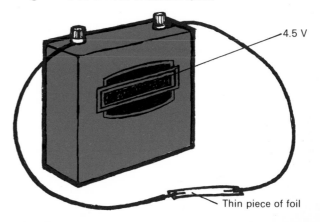

4.5 V

Thin piece of foil

## What will electricity pass through?

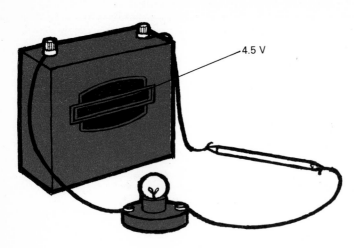

4.5 V

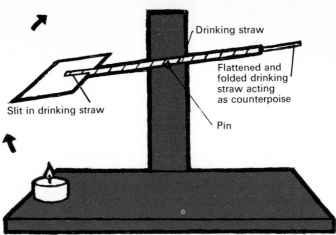

Drinking straw

Flattened and folded drinking straw acting as counterpoise

Pin

Slit in drinking straw

Try a pencil connected to a battery and bulb.

If children become really interested in finding out about electricity there are further suggestions in *Early experiences* and *Science from toys*.

### Ventilation grilles
Where are these?

Why do we need a hole high up on the wall?

Why do we often open the top windows in preference to others?

This leads to work on air currents. Take the temperature at different places in the classroom, near the floor, over the radiator, below the door, near the ventilator and as near the ceiling as possible.

Where is the room warmest?

What does this tell us about the way heat is distributed in the classroom?

The effect of warm air rising is easily demonstrated by setting up a balance as shown in the diagram and placing a nightlight below the piece of card.

Another favourite way of showing it is by cutting out a snake from paper or aluminium kitchen foil and suspending this by cotton above a nightlight or a radiator. As the warm air rises it causes the snake to revolve on the cotton.

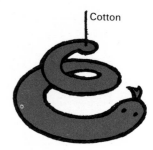

Cotton

Talk about air currents through the room.

Where are there likely to be draughts?

Where do children find draughts at home?

Why is there sometimes a large draught if you sit between the door and the fireplace?

Heating grilles occur in many modern schools. Look at where these are placed and where the grilles that allow the air to leave the classroom occur.

Visit the boiler-house. Trace the pipes or heating ducts through the school. Make a plan.

## Look for holes outdoors

What about holes around the school? How many different kinds can be found on a walk? Make a list.

### Manholes

There are manholes with a multiplicity of different covers. A 'collection' of such covers could be made by covering them with large sheets of paper and taking rubbings with cobbler's wax or crayons. Alternatively, you can rub over the paper with candle wax and then paint in the areas between the wax.

What are the covers made of?

What markings do they have on them?

What is the purpose of all these covers?

Do they lead to the drains, to the water supply, to coal-holes, to electrical cables, to the gas mains, or to the telephone cables? Can more be found out about the pipes or conduits beneath manhole covers?

A coal-hole cover rubbing

9

Coal-hole covers abound throughout the country, especially in cities such as London, Bristol, Bath, Manchester and Liverpool. Very early ones were rectangular without a great deal of design. These broke easily at the corners and the later circular iron plates with geometric designs are more common.

Try dating your covers. Firms names can often be traced to an old Kelly's street directory at the library. This should tell when the firm was in operation. Some of the covers have patent numbers on them and these can be traced at the Patent Office in London.

## A hole in the road

Workmen may be digging a hole in the road. There are many possibilities here (see *Structures and forces Stages 1 & 2*).

To take just one example, how many different materials are used? What can you find out about each of these materials? Concrete is made from stone chippings, sand and cement. What proportions do the workmen use?

Where are there holes in buildings? What are these holes for? What sort of things pass through them? If the holes carry pipes, are these pipes bringing things into the house or taking things away?

## Tunnels

Where is the nearest tunnel to your school? Draw a map of your area and mark in all the tunnels.

What are they made of? What goes through them?

Most tunnels have a curved, arched roof. Why?

Try experimenting with tunnel-shaped structures made of card.

Tunnels through hard rock are usually this shape.

Pressure

Tunnels through soft rock are usually round.

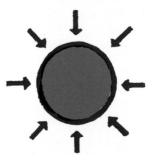

Pressure all round

What shape are the tunnels in your area?

What are tunnels lined with? Which is the longest tunnel in Great Britain? . . . in the world? (See the *Guinness Book of Records*.)

Don't forget there are tunnels we never see. There are a large number throughout the world, for example to conduct water from reservoirs to turn turbines.

Coins

Wood block nailed to base    Baseboard    Which tunnel will support most coins?

## Reservoirs

These are usually blocked off valleys. Sometimes they have a clay-lined bottom.

Make a saucer-like structure from clay and fill it with water. Leave it for some hours. Does the water seep through?

On a large scale it would be fun to make a model reservoir in the school grounds. A sloping piece of ground or a sand-pit would be ideal. Scoop out the earth or sand, line the bottom with clay, which is well tamped in, and build a dam wall across the front. If this latter structure is made of concrete so much the better but it could be quickly made up with a piece of planking. You might even put some aquatic plants in.

A dam wall is thicker at its base than at its top. Why is this? What about some of the famous dams in the world? Where are they and how big are they?

Make a map showing the distribution of reservoirs supplying water to your area.

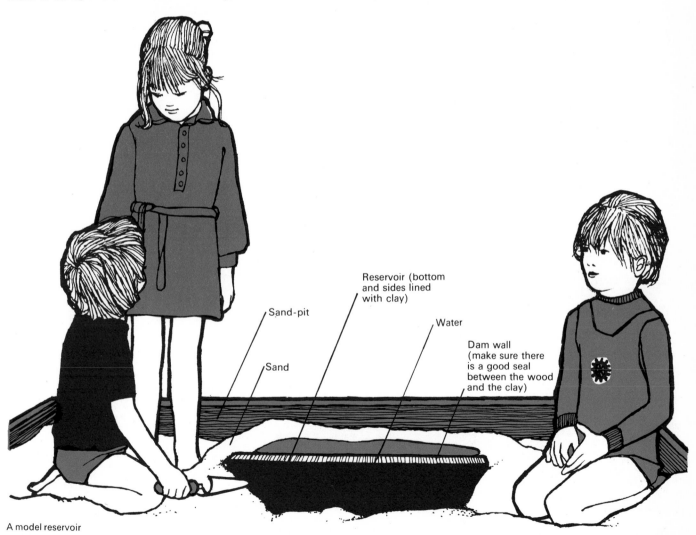

Sand-pit

Sand

Reservoir (bottom and sides lined with clay)

Water

Dam wall (make sure there is a good seal between the wood and the clay)

A model reservoir

### Shafts and mines

Schools in mining areas might do a lot of work in this field.

How is a shaft sunk?

How do the galleries spread out in a mine?

How is the roof supported?

What equipment is used?

Even children in the London area can become involved for the Science Museum has a large scale model coal mine which they can explore.

Try and find out the deepest shaft sunk by man (*Guinness Book of Records*). Make a clay ball to represent the earth, remember the earth's diameter is approximately 13 000 km (8 000 miles). Keeping the scale you have chosen push in a pin to represent man's deepest hole. Does it go very far?

### Quarries

Here, often lie history and evolution on one's doorstep. These large man-made cavities expose the surface layers of soil and the bedrock beneath.

What kinds of rock are there?

How were they formed?

Are the rocks in layers?

How do the layers lie in relation to one another?

How old are the rocks and do they contain fossils?

If it's an old quarry are there signs of erosion or has recolonisation by plants begun? If so, what sorts of plants are present?

The multifarious lines of evolution, the time sequence in which rock layers were formed, the crystalline structure of rock, earth movements and weathering might all arise and develop from a class visit.

### Vehicles

Look at vehicles and consider the function of the holes in them. One school looked at a car. This led to a discussion on the exhaust, clock, locks, petrol cap, mats, radio, grille, heater, dashboard and so on.

## Make some holes

There are many ways to make a hole. Some, like digging, are primitive and basic to man, others, like drilling and blasting, are more recent and spectacular.

How many ways can children find of making a hole? This will set them thinking about how often man does in fact need to make holes and how useful such holes can be. Begin with a class discussion or simply by providing a lot of material such as nails, screws, drills, hammers, a brace and a bit and so on. A nice demonstration that can be done by the teacher in a boiler-house, is to bore a hole through wood with a red-hot poker—it makes a lovely smell.

### Make holes in paper

An activity that children adore from early childhood is folding and tearing paper to make patterns. Such patterns are usually symmetrical and may lead off into considering symmetry in general (see *Structures and forces Stages 1 & 2*).

A punch is often used to perforate paper for a loose-leaf file. Children might make up a punch code and perforate pieces of card to send messages. What link has this got with a computer?

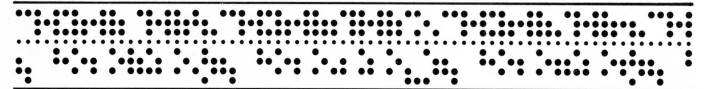

A computer tape

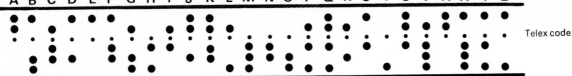

A B C D E F G H I J K L M N O P Q R S T U V W X Y Z

Telex code

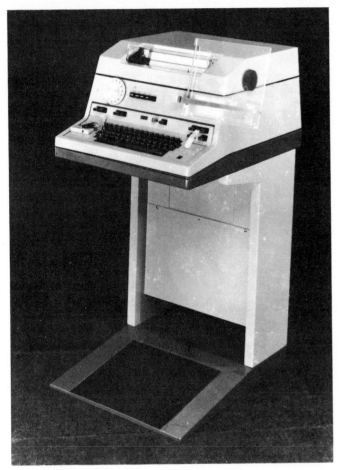

A Telex machine

A Telex machine is rather like a typewriter and with it messages are sent along ordinary telephone lines. The machine punches holes in a paper tape when a message is being sent. The pattern of holes represents letters and words.

Make up some messages using Telex code. How many other ways can you find of sending messages?

## Make holes in clay or Plasticine

Pushing a finger into clay makes a hole. Prodding with a pencil point first and then the flat end tells something of the pressure needed. At a more sophisticated level investigation might be made of the depth penetrated in relation to the force applied.

How far will a pencil penetrate a block of clay if successive weights, say 100 g, 200 g, 500 g, 1000 g, are rested on top of it?

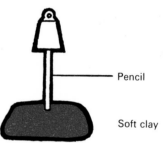

Pencil

Soft clay

Depth of penetration against weight applied can be plotted. What happens if you keep the weight constant but change the cross-sectional area of the prodder. For example, you might use prodders of 1 cm², 2 cm², 4 cm² and so on.

A heavier weight might be needed. A brick might do.

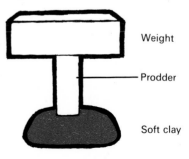

Weight

Prodder

Soft clay

Can you work out the pressure in grammes per square centimetre?

See *Working with wood Stages 1 & 2* for children's investigation about making holes in timber.

## Dig some holes

People are always digging holes—to put in foundations, rob a bank or bring a road under a river.

Visit a building site and look at all the tools and machines used for digging holes. Make a list. There are shovels, picks and mechanical diggers to loosen the earth. Bulldozers, cranes with buckets and lorries to carry it away. Make some models of the machines you see.

Dig a hole in the school grounds. Try using shovels, forks and trowels. How does the shape of the implement help in the digging process?

What sort of soil have you got at school? Is it sandy or clayey? Try rolling the soil in your hand.

1  Soil will not form into a sausage shape   SANDY SOIL
   Soil will roll into a sausage shape                2

2  Sausage shape bends into a ring       CLAY SOIL
   Sausage shape will not bend into a ring     3

3  Soil feels gritty               SANDY LOAM
   Soil feels silky               CLAY LOAM

Make a nice sharp edge to your hole and have a closer look at the soil.

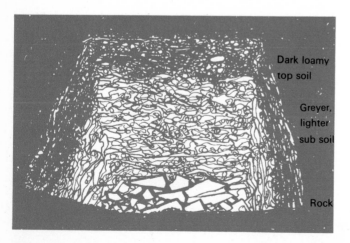

Dark loamy top soil

Greyer, lighter sub soil

Rock

The top soil will probably be fairly black because it is rich in decaying plant material. It may contain animals which are themselves worth looking at.

Look at the vegetation growing on this loamy soil. Plants like daisies will have short rooting systems whilst dandelions will have long tap-roots penetrating the soil. Grass will have a fibrous mass of roots on the soil surface.

Feel a handful of this soil and compare it with the lighter subsoil which is lacking in organic matter.

If the soil cover is not too deep you may find some ground rock from which the soil particles might have been derived. It's useful to point out to children that soil is only a sophisticated form of rock.

## Making a record

Roll a sheet of clear acetate to form a tube, which is the depth of the hole, and seal it firmly with Sellotape.

Use a trowel to remove the soil, a little at a time, from a vertical section down the side of the hole and put it into the tube. Seal the bottom and put some vegetation on the top soil.

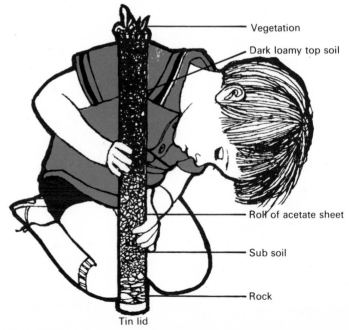

Vegetation

Dark loamy top soil

Roll of acetate sheet

Sub soil

Rock

Tin lid

This chapter has been concerned with making a beginning and many starting points are suggested in the text.

Here to conclude the chapter is a flow chart showing the way one class developed its work on holes, gaps and cavities.

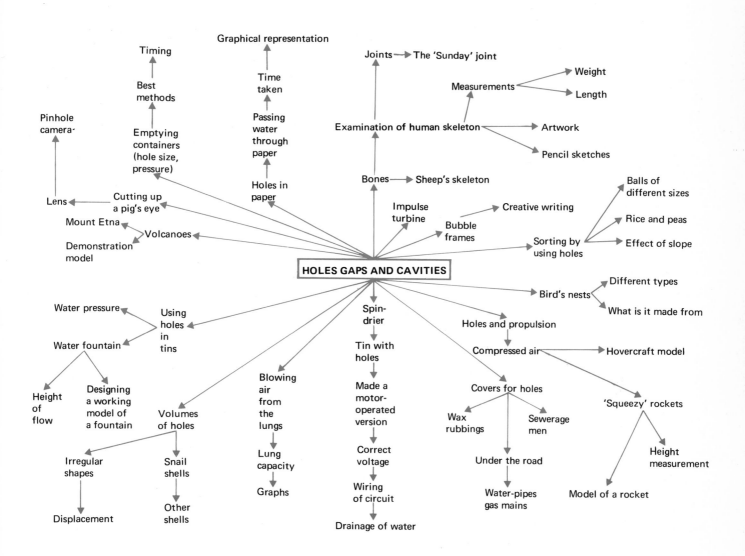

Many of the points in this flow chart are taken up in the succeeding chapters.

# Holes and air

Have a look at holes that air passes through.

## Holes and things that move

An easy way to get started is by making some models that move. Why not begin with a parachute? Try some made from polythene sheeting.

### Parachutes

Try finding out which of these parachutes is more efficient? What causes this?

Try and obtain *fabric with a loose weave*. Make a

parachute with this. Does it need a hole? Make a series of parachutes with centre holes of differing diameter.

Time the descent of each parachute from a fixed mark. For example try and throw each parachute as high as the guttering on a building or drop them from an upper storey window.

Of course there will need to be discussion on whether the parachutes have to be the same size and whether it is better to time one or several descents of each parachute. If their weights differ does it make a difference? Plot a graph of time of descent against diameter of hole. Plot a graph of time of descent against number of washers tied to the end of the parachute.

## Hovercraft

A hovercraft moves on a cushion of air which is retained beneath the vehicle. Models which children can easily make usually only show how air acts as a lubricant.

Start by making a hole in the centre of a plastic margarine container.

Blow here

Blow air through it by using a cardboard tube, a toilet-roll centre will do.

What happens to the 'hovercraft'?

A more sophisticated version can be made from a circular disc cut from card or hardboard. You might also use a small gramophone record.

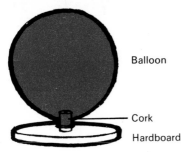

Balloon

Cork

Hardboard

Make a hole at the centre of your piece of card. Drill a hole through a cork. Glue this over the hole in the card.

Blow up a balloon, pinch its neck and fit it over the cork.

Let go.

Give the hovercraft a push and watch it travel over the floor.

## Rockets and jet propulsion

Rockets have holes through which jets of hot gases escape. They work on the principle of jet propulsion.

If you blow up a balloon and pinch the neck the air presses equally in all directions.

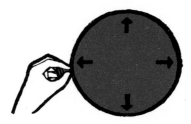

When the neck is released air rushes out and there is no longer any backward pressure. The forward pressure of air on the balloon remains the same however and it travels forward. Try it and see.

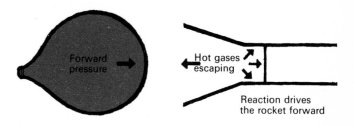

Forward pressure

Hot gases escaping

Reaction drives the rocket forward

Balloon

Rocket

Rockets work on the same principle.

Collect pictures of rockets and try and find out more about their structure and the way they work.

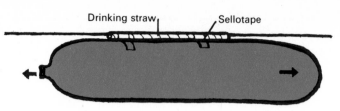

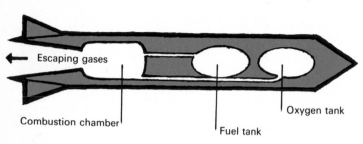

Why does a rocket carry oxygen? Where does the fuel in a jet plane get its oxygen from? What sort of guidance system is there in a rocket?

Firework rockets work on much the same principle.

With a great deal of perseverance it is possible to plot the distance travelled against the diameter of the balloon.

Don't forget that nature was a long time ahead of man with jet propulsion. Look at a picture of a squid and try and find out how it moves.

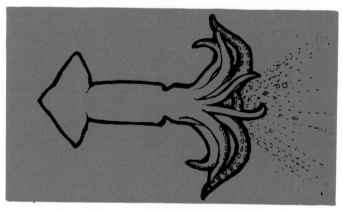

A simple model worked by a water jet is shown below.

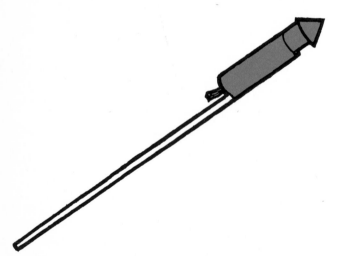

Where is the guidance system here?

It might be useful to try out ways to guide the direction of the flight of a balloon. One well-known way is to Sellotape a sausage-shaped balloon to a drinking straw and thread it on a line stretched tightly across the classroom.

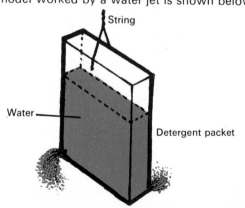

# Holes and sounds

## Holes and making sounds

Sounds are caused by vibrations. In many musical instruments the sound comes from a vibrating column of air as in an organ-pipe or a recorder for example.

Blow across the top of a milk bottle. What sort of sound do you get? Does it remind you of wind across a chimney top?

Blow across the top of a milk bottle containing water. What sound do you get now? Blow gently. Blow hard. What differences do you get? Line up a series of milk bottles and fill them with varying amounts of water so that by tapping you produce a scale.

Make a drinking straw whistle:

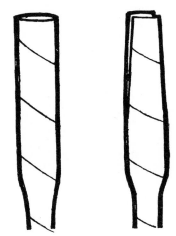

Flatten about 3 cm of the end of a drinking straw.

Cut a tiny strip about 2 cm long from each side.

Put the flattened end of the drinking straw right inside your mouth and blow. Keep trying until you get a sound.

Put your tongue very gently against the end of the straw as you blow. What do you feel? What is happening to the air in the tube? What happens if you shorten the length of your straw?

Make a series of drinking straw whistles each 2 cm shorter than the next.

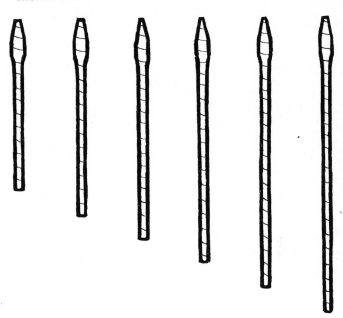

Which gives the highest note?

Which gives the lowest note?

Look at some pipes of Pan.

It should now become clear that vibrations are needed to make sounds and that a long column of vibrating air will produce low notes whilst a short column of vibrating air will produce high notes. Have a look at a recorder and note the effect of changing the length of the column of air in this. It's also worth noting that different *sizes* of holes are drilled in recorders and other wind instruments.

Make a list of all the musical instruments that have a column of vibrating air in them when they are played. What is each one made of? How is the length of the column of air in each one altered?

Make drawings or collect pictures of all these instruments.

# Holes and catching sounds
Well there's the ear to start with.

## Ears and ear trumpets
Have a look at animals. Can you classify them? Perhaps into those with ears and those that do not appear to have ears. What does a dog do when it hears a sound?

The trumpet can also be used as a megaphone.

Make up a way to find out if the megaphone carries your voice over a distance. Some orchestral instruments have trumpet-like openings. Why?

## Speaking tubes
In Victorian times speaking tubes were very popular. A hole to speak into and a hole to listen at. You will need a long length of rubber tubing or a hose-pipe and two squeezy bottles to make one.

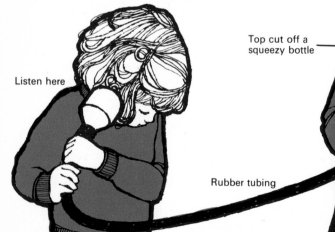

Listen here

Top cut off a squeezy bottle

Speak here

Rubber tubing

## Stethoscopes
Doctors use stethoscopes. Again it is easy to improvise one.

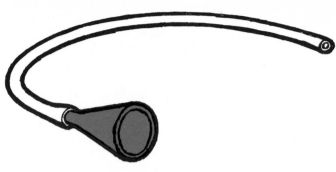

## Catching sounds outdoors
The microphone on a tape recorder will pick up sounds. Try picking up sounds outdoors. Can you record someone talking across the other side of the playground.

Try using the reflector from a car headlight.

Place the microphone where the filament of the lamp would be.

Reflector

Microphone

Does this help? If so, why?

Most people at one time or another have used the cavity in a seashell to listen to the 'sound of the sea'. What they really hear is the sound made by the blood corpuscles as they pass through the blood vessels of the ear.

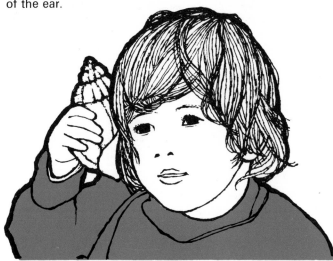

The shell catches sound and throws it back into the ear. People with very sensitive hearing can hear this without the aid of a shell if they sit in a quiet room.

## Holes and air pressure

### A bicycle pump

We're often pushing air through holes. Many vehicles travel on pneumatic tyres and keeping these up to the right pressure is important. Have a look at a bicycle pump. If you put a finger over the hole at the end and press the handle in what will happen?

Washer

Take a pump to pieces. Can you find out how the air is pushed out at the end of the pump?

What is the purpose of the washer? What happens if you reverse the washer and put it in the other way round?

Have a look at the bicycle valve that fits into the tyre. That has a hole in it too. Can you find out how the valve works?

### A Cartesian diver

Take a medicine dropper and fill it with water until it just floats in a bowl of water.

Then transfer it to a bottle full of water.

Put in a cork and gently press on it.

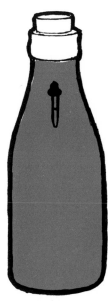

What happens to the diver? Why is this?

Does carefully watching the water level in the dropper help you in reaching an explanation?

## Holes and bubbles

A joined forefinger and thumb, pipes, drinking straws, wire loops and so on can be used as frames for blowing bubbles. All sorts of frames can be made from bent wire.

Blow large bubbles and small bubbles. Does the colour of a bubble vary with its size? What happens when a bubble hits a table-top? Look closely.

Try sticking a pin, very gently, into a bubble. What do you notice at the point where the pin meets the bubble?

Bubble frames

Start with the hole in a simple wire loop. Dip the loop into very soapy water (use washing-up liquid). Look at the soap film. What colours are in it? Blow gently. Blow hard. What happens?

Blow down a drinking straw into a bowl of soapy water. Look at the pattern of bubbles on the water surface. What happens at the surfaces where bubble meets bubble?

## Cavities and air—a situation for the sink

Modern ships, especially the new oil tankers, are gigantic hollow metal vessels filled with air. A ship weighs the same as the amount of water it pushes out of place and it is held up by the thrust of the water. The thrust upwards of the water and the weight of the ship balance exactly. The concepts involved are beyond most children at Stage 2 but the experiences are not and the whole problem is worth investigating.

With young children try a range of objects in water in a large sink or bowl and sort out those that float from those that sink. Some objects such as large tin lids, toy boats, plastic bottle tops, ice-cream cartons and so on will both float and sink depending on whether their cavities are full of water or not.

Make paper boats, Plasticine boats, balsa wood boats and kitchen foil boats.

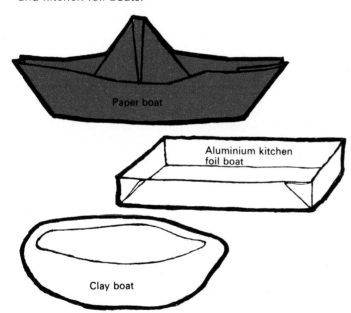

Paper boat

Aluminium kitchen foil boat

Clay boat

How many different-shaped boats can be made?

How many different materials can be used to make boats?

## Boats of Plasticine

Plasticine is very malleable and easily made up into boats of differing shape. Ask the children to make up their own boats and find out which shape is most stable in water.

Which shape is best? A bowl shape? A saucer shape? A square box? A canoe shape? What happens if you screw the boat into a ball?

Which shape is best?

If possible use luke-warm water to float the boats in because Plasticine becomes hard and unmanageable when cold water is used. It's also best to start each time with fresh Plasticine as damp Plasticine tends to develop holes.

Look at the sides of the boats. How high do they need to be? What happens if they get too high?

Loading the boat: load the boat with objects from pockets. Who can get most objects into a boat? Is this because of the shape of the boat or because of its size? Perhaps both these factors play a part. Here is the opportunity for a worthwhile discussion. It could lead to more controlled experimenting. Try, for example, loads of known weight. Perhaps nails or washers would do.

Have a competition to find who can make a boat to carry most washers.

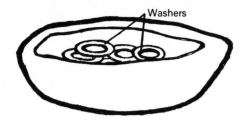

Washers

Do all children in the competition need to have the same amount of Plasticine? Do washers have to be placed in carefully or can they just be dropped in? What about the placing of the washers in the boat—does it affect stability?

Compare the boats at the end of the competition and draw up a list showing all the factors necessary for making a boat capable of holding the most washers.

Make the *same size* hole in each of your boats. Which is the quickest one to sink?

## Boats made from things lying around
Try floating yogurt, ice-cream, cream and potted shrimp cartons. Try frozen food trays and foil pie cases as well. Look carefully at their shapes and capacities.

How many washers do you think each will hold before it sinks?

Was it a good guess?

Do you get better as you move from one container to another?

Will a metal foil case (a milk bottle top will do) float if you crumple it up lightly?

What happens if you make it into a tight metal ball?

Try floating a range of stoppered bottles. How much water must you put in each so that it floats upright? How much so that it just floats?

Try some tin cans.

How much water does each need to make it float upright?

How much water does it need to make it *just* sink?

Try various heights of tin but keep the diameter constant.

## Diving bells
An enclosed cavity is found in a diving bell.

Put a handkerchief in the bottom of a jam jar and plunge it mouth downwards into a bucket of water.

Handkerchief

The handkerchief keeps dry. Why is this?
What keeps the water out?

This, of course, brings up the realm of caissons and discussion of 'the bends' when nitrogen bubbles into the blood of a diver if the pressure is reduced too quickly as he is brought up.

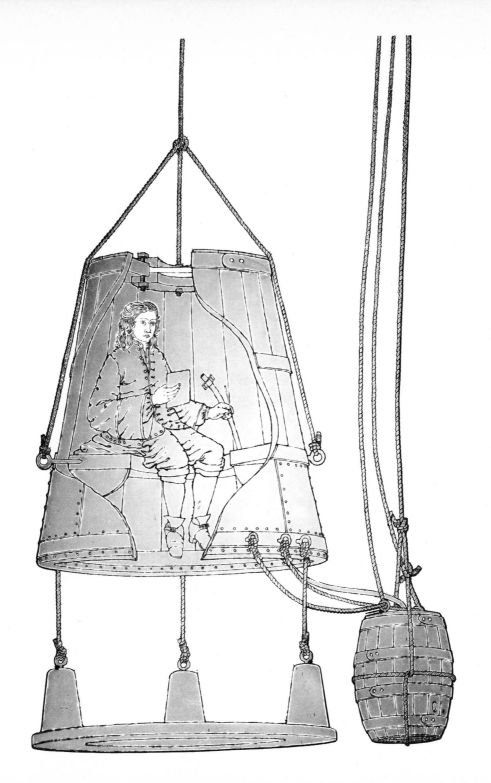

An early diving bell

# Flowing out of holes

## Drops from holes

Another way to begin might be to consider the way liquids flow out of holes in containers. If you start with something as simple as a drinking straw it is relatively easy to see what happens if water flows from its end.

### Drinking straws
Dip a drinking straw into water and then close your finger over the free end of the straw. Remove the

straw from the water. Water remains within the straw. (This might be a suitable time to digress and talk about 'air pressure', and perhaps carry out work on that topic.) Take the drinking straw and make a small drop of water on the desk or table-top.

What shape is the drop of water? What happens if you put two drops so close that they touch? Make a pile of drops. Does it get higher? Does it get wider? How high does it get before it spills over?

Now make a line of drops with your drinking straw.

Are they all the same size? If not, what might you do to get the smallest possible drop with your drinking straw?

What must you do to get the largest possible drop with your drinking straw?

Can you with practice, get a line of drops all the same size?

Think of other devices that can be used to make drops. A cocktail stick or a pin, for example.

Who is the champion maker of the smallest drops in the class?

What about other liquids? Try making large and small drops and piles of drops with water, water to which a detergent has been added, vinegar, cooking-oil or even syrup. The height which a pile of drops will reach depends on the density and viscosity (thickness) of the liquid and its surface tension (stickiness).

## Different surfaces

Put some water drops on different surfaces such as wood (plain, varnished and painted), glass, Formica, waxed paper, newspaper, notepaper, aluminium kitchen foil, a plastic bag, rubber, leather, fabrics and so on—include your own skin. How does the surface affect the size and shape of each drop? Try other liquids.

## Drop size

Look at the size of drops more critically. Compare, for example, the size of water-drops with the size of

cooking-oil drops. If a large number were compared the difference is easier to see. It may be more accurate to use a medicine dropper to do this.

Compare 100 drops of water with 100 drops of cooking-oil.

Alka-Seltzer tube (or any other narrow container)

Water                    Cooking-oil

Why is it best to use the same dropper in each case?

Do the liquids reach the same level in each tube or do they differ?

If they differ which liquid has the largest drop size?

Try other liquids.

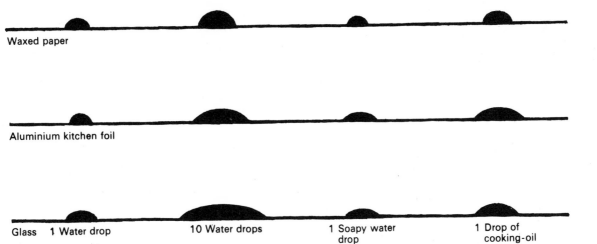

Waxed paper

Aluminium kitchen foil

Glass    1 Water drop        10 Water drops        1 Soapy water drop        1 Drop of cooking-oil

## Piling up

If children went on adding drops to each tube until they reached the hole at the top which tube would hold the most liquid? That is to say will water pile up higher at the top of the tube than will cooking-oil?

Compare water with soapy water or with vinegar.

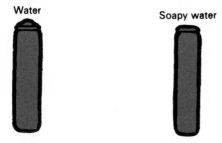

Water

Soapy water

Can children find any relationship between the height of a liquid at the top of a container and the shape of that liquid as drops?

Fill a cup brimful of water. How many pennies can you gently slip in before the water overflows?

## Some information

The viscosity ('thickness') and the surface tension ('stickiness') of a liquid retard it from overflowing. These forces together with density hold a water drop together as you make it bigger by adding small drops of water. The density and viscosity of ordinary water and soapy water are similar but their surface tension is very different. Water molecules are held together by strong forces which produce a 'skin' at the surface, the surface tension. When you add soap to water the soap molecules get in between the water molecules and reduce the forces holding them together. That is, the surface tension is reduced.

## Using holes to make things look bigger

Children often drip water on to a printed page. It is interesting to see what letters look like through a drop of water. Try looking at printing in a glossy magazine and at newsprint through the surface of a water drop. If you use soapy water does it make any difference? Such drops of water, of course, magnify.

Draw a small circle on a piece of glass with a crayon and fill this circle with water from a medicine dropper.

Mike is planning an extension into the back garden and talks casually of dropping the centre of the floor in the upstairs office down "a foot or so".

At 28 Morpeth Street, the last house in which they stayed long enough to accord it the title of a "base", Mike introduced into his room a lighting system of 20 different lamps which could be individually controlled from a panel by the bed. In addition the panel, with a total of 32 switches, could pipe stereo music into any upstairs room including the bathroom.

This year Mike and Pete's rooms in 28 Morpeth Street are occupied by

the answer in a bo install night storage a lot of laws abou kind of wiring so I don't understand it manual."

Pete, aged 25, is still a Geography the University. Besi of the manual lab books and general financial side of the ber last year Mike themselves into a books are at presen Recently they ha

*Glass sheet*  *Crayon*  *Water drop*

Use the water drop as a lens to examine writing. Find some very small print and look at it. The best way to do this is to place the piece of glass with the water drop over a printed word and slowly lift the glass until the word appears clearly. How many times wider do the letters appear?

Make a series of wax circles of differing size on your piece of glass and fill them all with water.

vide accommodation for students and give the Union a say in their policy of accommodation."

The money was given on 11 per cent. interest. Mike Dennis says: "Investing in us they're getting a return on their money and are alleviating one of the pressing needs, housing."

With the money they bought and refitted another six houses. It meant weeks of round-the-clock work and they employed no outside labour, although from time to time they were helped out by a number of student friends. At one point they were finishing off houses only a matter of

because it meant cratic trouble. Hu very helpful but yo apply in early sprin summer, and the query. We haven't before. Up to this fu education. grow m are beginning to lo sive properties in known as The Aven paid £3,000 for Avenue, almost twi have paid previousl

The house in Pa

Which of these 'lenses' stands up highest?

Which of them is most powerful?

Children might make a series of simple magnifiers from bent wire. Dip the wire into water and lift it out with a water drop clinging to the loop. Try glycerine, oil and other liquids to see what effect they give.

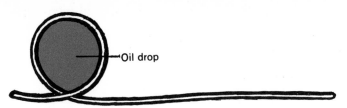

Oil drop

You might like to use a hole to make a quite powerful magnifier.

Take a strip of metal and make a hole in it with a nail and a hammer or a drill.

Cover this hole with a water drop.

Metal strip

This drop can be used to give a magnified image in the same way as the drop on the piece of glass.

It might be useful to mount it on a stand.

Instead of water try glycerine, cooking-oil or washing-up liquid to see what effects they give.

A match-box magnifier is fun to make.

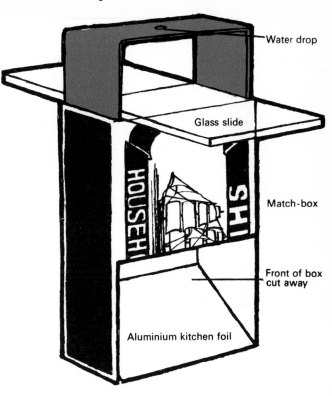

Water drop

Glass slide

Match-box

Front of box cut away

Aluminium kitchen foil

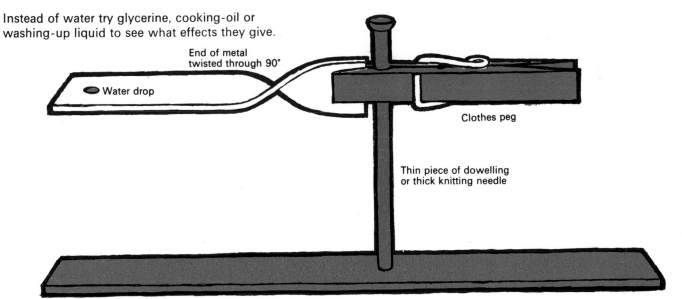

End of metal twisted through 90°

Water drop

Clothes peg

Thin piece of dowelling or thick knitting needle

## In and out of holes

### Out

Set up a number of containers near a large sink. Try to include wide and narrow, long and short ones and try and get a range of size in the hole at the top of the container. How many ways can children find to empty them? Make a list. Which is the quickest way to empty *each* container? Again make a list.

What effect does: raising, lowering, squeezing, shaking, tilting, rotating, have on the *time* of emptying?

### Making more holes to help liquids out

If it is possible make a hole in the base of a container and repeat the investigations suggested above. In other words how quickly can you empty a container with two holes? What about making holes in different places? What effect does this have?

How, for example, would the squeezy bottles pictured below empty if you make holes in the places suggested.

If you have a set of drills you might make a hole of fixed size, say 1·58 mm [$\frac{1}{16}$ in] in one squeezy bottle and a hole 3·17 mm [$\frac{1}{8}$ in] in a companion bottle.

Cap stuck firmly on

Which is the quickest way to empty each container?

Does the bottle empty twice as fast when the hole is twice as large? Be careful here! What is meant by twice as *large*? Is it diameter or area? This might be a very nice lead into the relationship between linear dimensions and area for some children.

What about different-shaped holes? Try a square hole, a triangular hole, a rectangular hole, an irregular-shaped hole.

Will hot water run out more quickly than cold? What about different liquids? Which will empty most *quickly*—a container full of water or a container full of soapy water? (Add only a small amount of detergent (a one percent solution) or too much foam might result.)

## In

Filling containers such as a bucket or a jam jar is easy but how would children fill a container with a narrow hole such as a scent bottle?

Will a sieve float? Try a heavy one, a light one, a very light one. How many ways can children think up of preventing water running through the holes in a sieve? Perhaps by lining the sieve with a water-repellant fabric or by rubbing a candle over the sieve surface.

### How much in?

Take a collection of bottles. Use the smallest bottle to calibrate the largest bottle. This might be done very quickly by sticking a piece of tape down the side of the large bottle and making a mark on it every time water is added from the smallest bottle. The large calibrated bottle can now be used to find the volume of the other containers.

Find out the cost of various liquids in the supermarket. Work out their cost per unit volume.

How does the cost per unit volume of a small bottle of lemonade compare with the cost per unit volume of a large bottle?

If you have three different-sized bottles of detergent which is the best buy?

## Holes and beading

If you hold a container high enough you may find the stream of water running out breaks into drops.

Collect six matched squeezy bottles and drills of varying sizes say 1·58 mm [$\frac{1}{16}$ in], 1·98 mm [$\frac{5}{64}$ in], 2·38 mm [$\frac{5}{32}$ in], 2·77 mm [$\frac{7}{64}$ in], 3·17 mm [$\frac{1}{8}$ in], 3·57 mm [$\frac{9}{64}$ in].

Drill a hole in the base of each bottle. Fill each bottle with water.

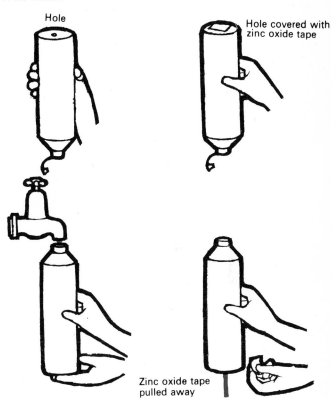

Hole

Hole covered with zinc oxide tape

Zinc oxide tape pulled away

The point at which each column of water breaks up will vary with the size of the hole.

Try to measure the length of the unbroken portion of the column, from each of the six squeezy bottles, as quickly as possible after it starts flowing.

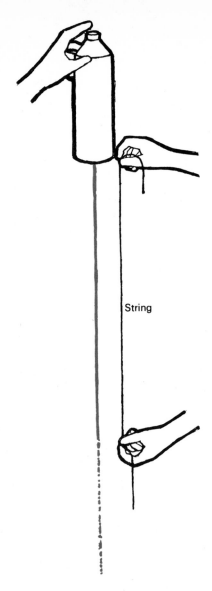

String

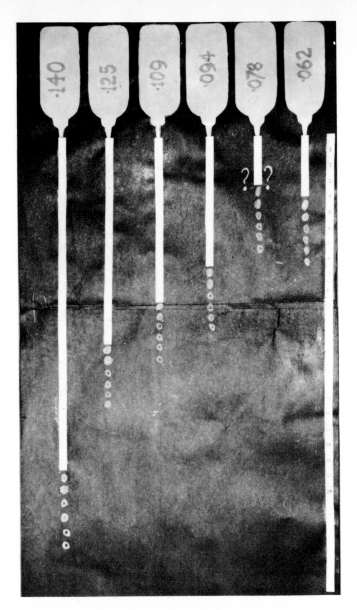

The effect of hole size on break up into drops of water

This might be done by holding a piece of string or ribbon alongside it.

A block graph can then be constructed of length of column plotted against size of hole.

If children cope successfully with this, it might be taken a stage further.

Can children suggest what else, other than the size of hole, will affect the point at which break up into drops occurs?

Squeezing the bottle, changing its height, using a different liquid (soapy water) might be investigated.

# Beading

Hole size increasing from left to right

Playground

Where does beading occur in each column?

How long does each take to empty?

How long does each take if filled with soapy water?

## Some information on beading

Molecules of water attract one another strongly. As the water falls from the squeezy bottle the molecules attract one another and the water tends to round off into drops.

The attraction of molecules also pulls the outer parts of the water column inward. This attraction decreases as the diameter of the column increases. Thicker columns therefore fall further before they break into drops.

Soapy water columns also fall further before breaking into drops than do columns of ordinary water. Here the soap molecules get in between the water molecules. This reduces attractive forces between the water molecules and tends to retard the point at which the water breaks into drops.

33

## Out into the playground with streams

A bucket of water and a squeezy bottle are all that are needed.

Try shooting streams at random from a squeezy bottle full of water.

Vary their height and direction.

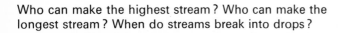

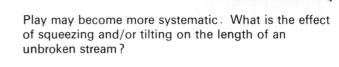

Who can make the highest stream? Who can make the longest stream? When do streams break into drops?

Play may become more systematic. What is the effect of squeezing and/or tilting on the length of an unbroken stream?

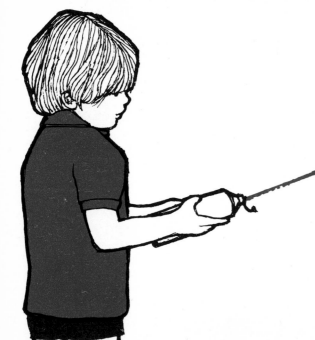

Can you hit a skittle by shooting from a fixed base-line?

If a partner varies the position of the skittle can the 'gunner' hit it first time?

Can you shoot an unbroken stream into a bucket of water?

What sort of noise does it make?

What sort of noise does a broken stream make?

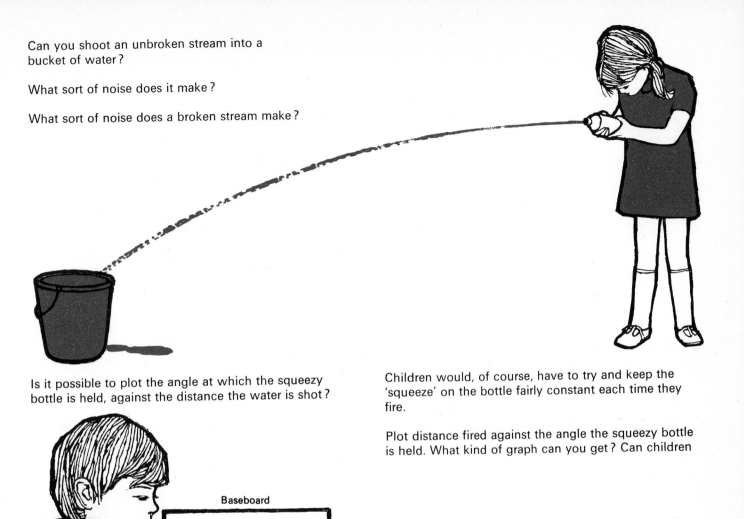

Is it possible to plot the angle at which the squeezy bottle is held, against the distance the water is shot?

This might be done by resting the bottle on a table and lining up a sighting mark on the squeezy bottle's side with a mark on a baseboard held alongside the bottle.

Children would, of course, have to try and keep the 'squeeze' on the bottle fairly constant each time they fire.

Plot distance fired against the angle the squeezy bottle is held. What kind of graph can you get? Can children work out from their graph how they might hit a target placed at a fixed distance? They might test out their calculations and see if they are right.

## Other factors

Of course there are other factors that might affect streams:

What sort of streams does soapy water make?

What effect does sand, mixed up with water, have on the streams?

What effect does wind have on the stream?

What happens to streams when they meet different surfaces? Try a brick wall, a concrete surface, painted and unpainted wood, windows, a tree trunk, wire netting and so on.

What happens to streams when they meet one another?

## A hose pipe

Many of these squeezy bottle activities with streams can be repeated with a hose pipe. The scale is grander, more eloquent and even more fun. It is well worth trying to borrow one.

## Fountains

Water pressure due to the weight of the water itself can be used to make a fountain.

**Ball-point pen with ink reservoir removed**

What happens as you raise the container and increase the pressure? Does the height of the water change? What happens if you lower the container below the jet? Or water can be forced up.

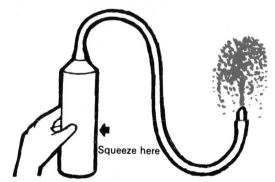

Squeeze here

This force can be quite large—large enough even to raise a child. Set up a hot water bottle connected to a large biscuit tin as shown. Put a tray on top of the hot-water bottle and let a child sit on it.

What happens if you raise the biscuit tin and wait for the water to flow into the bottle?

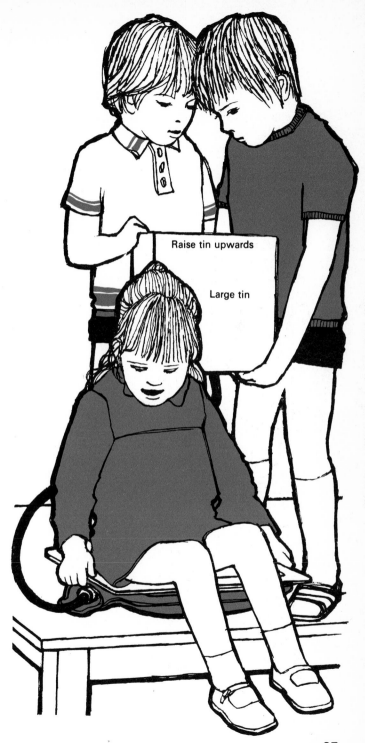

Raise tin upwards

Large tin

## Holes, water and steam

### Holes filled with water

Infants in their water play become aware that water takes up the shape of the vessel that contains it. The earth itself is full of large and small holes, gaps and cavities and very often these are filled with water.

Look at maps of the world and see how the water in oceans, seas and lakes takes up the shape of the cavity it fills.

Try and get some large-scale maps of the local area around the school.

How many holes, gaps and cavities do they show? Remember a lot of these will be filled with water.

Are any of these cavities regular? Invariably these will be man-made: canals and railway cuttings for example.

Why does water collect in certain holes?

Trace the path of streams from highland to lakes or to rivers and perhaps out to sea.

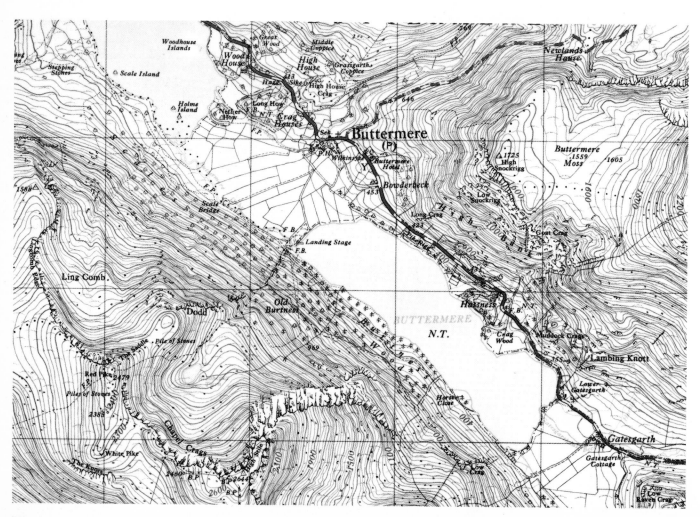

Lots of rainwater, of course, soaks directly into the soil. In some areas, limestone districts for example, the rain permeates quickly through the soil. If it hits an impermeable layer such as clay, it may come to the surface through a spring. Try this easy demonstration.

Cut off the tops of two squeezy bottles. Make a large number of holes in the bottom of each one. Fill one with sand. Put a layer of clay in the base of the other and then fill it with sand. Pour water through each.

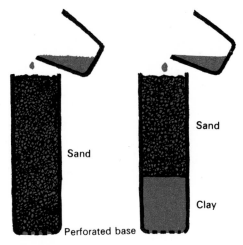

Sand

Sand

Clay

Perforated base

What happens?

Now make a hole in the side of the squeezy bottle containing clay just above the clay layer.

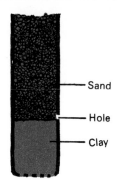

— Sand

— Hole

— Clay

What happens?

Are there any springs or wells in the district around the school?

## Water to the school

Such work often leads to a consideration of the local water supply.

What are the sources of local water?

Reservoirs, wells, springs, rivers may all figure.

How is the water carried across the countryside?

Where are pumps used?

What do the 3 and the 4 mean on this water hydrant plate?

Do some places within your area need water towers?

How is water purified (see 'Holes and sorting').

How is water brought into the school?

Where is the nearest water hydrant to the school?

What marks the exact spot?

Trace the water system through the building, don't forget to visit the boiler-house. Make a plan to show the way the pipes go.

## Using holes to do some work

Great use is made of steam power, usually by harnessing jets of steam as they shoot out of holes. This may be done in a simple reaction turbine, often called Hero's engine, or in an impulse turbine. Here are ways to make models of these machines.

REMEMBER THE DANGER WHERE STEAM IS USED—CAREFUL SUPERVISION WILL BE NEEDED WHEN TRYING OUT THE MODELS. KEEP HANDS AWAY FROM THE STEAM. DO NOT LET THE TIN BOIL DRY.

### Impulse turbine

Cut a circle from aluminium kitchen foil. Its size will vary with the size of the can that is used. Cut slits into it in order to make vanes.

Twist the vanes around the central axis and put it on a knitting needle as shown.

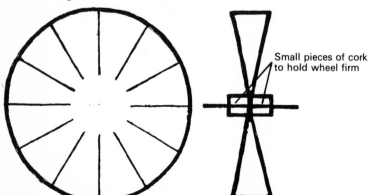

Small pieces of cork to hold wheel firm

It can be held in place with corks and mounted over a can.

Make sure it spins freely.

Metal strip

Hole to allow steam out

String

One group of children mounted their tin in a slightly different way.

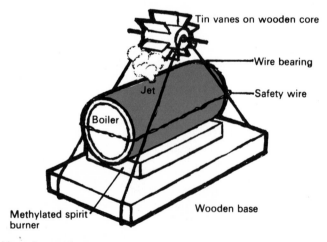

Tin vanes on wooden core

Wire bearing

Safety wire

Jet

Boiler

Methylated spirit burner

Wooden base

### Hero's engine

Make two slits (about 1·5 mm [$\frac{1}{16}$ in] wide) on either side of a tin can. Look at the diagram carefully to see the way they face.

Twist a circle of wire around the can to act as a support on which it can be hung.

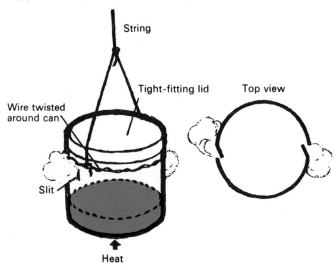

About a quarter fill the can with water. Fit the lid on tightly and heat the can.

It should spin on the string once the water boils. Can you tell which way it will spin before the water starts boiling?

## Moving things with steam

A group of children decided to make a steam-driven trolley. They made a wooden trolley and mounted a tin can over a methylated spirit burner as shown below.

This vehicle did not move under steam power. The children came to the conclusion that there was too much friction. The wheels were removed from the base and the base itself cut into a rough boat shape. The boat was tried on the school swimming pool.

It sank.

Sides were made for the boat.

It now floated safely but travelled in circles. So a rudder was added.

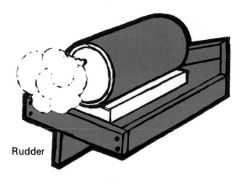

The boat was timed travelling down the pool.

A series of tins of the same size were obtained. The first had one hole in it, the second two, the third three and so on. The time taken to travel the length of the pool was plotted against the number of holes in the tin and a graph drawn.

# Letting light through

## The eye

Light travels through the pupils of eyes. The pupil rarely strikes children as being a hole and the easiest way to show this is to cut up a bullock's eye. Such eyes are usually easily obtained from the butcher or the local abattoir. The only equipment needed is a sharp pair of scissors, with good points, a large pin and a shallow dish, a pie-dish is excellent.

### Looking at the eye
Locate the optic nerve in the back lower half of the eye. It usually appears as a shiny, solid rod about 6·35 mm [$\frac{1}{4}$ in] diameter. Often it is hidden amongst the muscle and fat covering the eye and has to be 'dug' for.

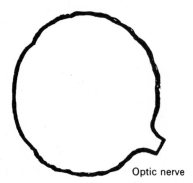

Side view

Cut away with scissors the muscle and fat covering the eye in order to expose its shape. The eye will then appear as a spherical body bulging slightly at the front.

The front of the eye has a transparent cover, the cornea, which may well have become opaque in the eye you are cutting up. Insert the point of the scissors under this and cut completely around the cornea.

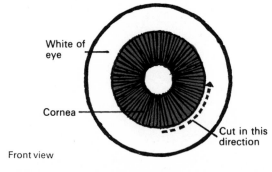

White of eye

Cornea

Cut in this direction

Front view

In doing this a watery fluid, the aqueous humour, will run out of the front part of the eye. The iris (the coloured part of the eye) and the pupil (a hole) will now be visible. Usually the surface of the lens shows behind the pupil.

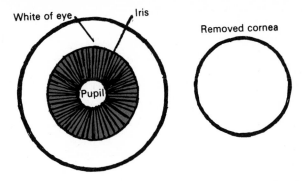

The front chamber of the eye has now been completely removed.

The remainder of the eye can be simply divided in two by cutting directly across the top and the bottom of the eye to the optic nerve.

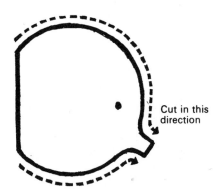

A thick jelly-like substance, the vitreous humour, will be found filling the eye and helping to give it shape. The wall of the eye will be found to be in three layers. The innermost of these is the light sensitive layer, the retina, which is very thin and delicate (it may well come away as a 'skin' on the vitreous humour). It is easy to lift off with the pin exposing the middle, black layer of the eye which is called the choroid layer. This layer prevents reflection of any light that passes through the retina. The third, outermost layer of the eye is thickest and constitutes the white of the eye, it is called the sclerotic layer.

The lens can easily be removed from the eye

and washed.

Place it on a printed letter in a textbook and note the effect.

> destined to become the centre of oper-
> ations. Until now have had to
> exist in varyi **th** f squalor
> because they **ve** ing in the
> often-derelict h have been
> working on.
>
> Now plans are afoot to convert the
> Park Avenue house into "the sort of
> place to which you can invite a bank
>
> Jane D'Arcy and
> two 21-year-old stu
> Mike is the ha
> virtually no previou
> supervised the r
> plumbing of up to
> serious hitches.
>
> He explains: "W
> something I don't

## How the pupil works

The pupil as well as being a hole for letting light through has a light regulating function. This is easy to demonstrate.

Place a mirror in a darkened corner, or other place with a dim light (a store cupboard might do). Get one child to look at his eyes in the mirror and a second child suddenly to shine a torch across *not into* the first child's eyes. What happens?

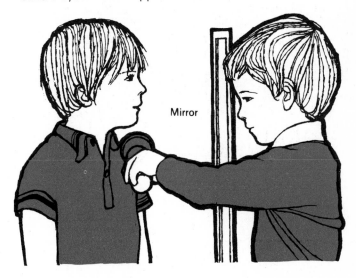

Mirror

You may prefer to do it by putting a hand over one eye, looking towards the window and waiting. Let a child observe the eye as you suddenly remove your hand.

What happens to the pupils? Keep watching. What do the pupils do as the seconds slowly pass?

Lots of other work might result. What are the eyes of other animals like? Draw a cat's eye during the day and at dusk. Does the pupil shape and size differ? Much discussion can result from drawing animal eyes on a visit to a zoo.

Finding out simple things about the eye intrigues children. The following are some suggestions.

### Which eye do you use most?
Line a pencil up with the edge of a window or door frame using both eyes. Close your right eye. Open it. Now close your left eye. Usually the pencil jumps sharply to one side when one of the eyes is closed. This is the eye that was used to line up the pencil, and the eye that is used most.

### Why two eyes?
A task for two children, each with a pencil. One child holds a pencil, point uppermost, at various distances in front of his partner. This latter child, with right eye closed, tries to touch the point of his partner's pencil with his own. Try the left eye. Now try with both eyes open.

Depth of vision is extremely important, just think how often one uses it during the day.

### Finding the 'blind spot'
The area of the retina where the optic nerve leaves the eye has no light sensitive cells and is consequently called the 'blind spot'. Its inability to respond to light rays can be demonstrated in the following way.

**X**

Move the book away from the right eye with the left eye closed. If you look fixedly at the X the black spot will seem to disappear. Light rays from this region are now falling on the 'blind spot'. Try doing this on a large scale with marks on the blackboard.

## Optical illusions

These are popular with children.

Which line is longest?

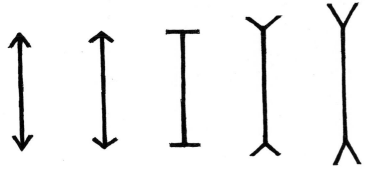

What do you see in the following picture—a girl or an old crone?

Make up your own illustrations.

## Cameras

Everyone of us has probably made use of an important application of light passing through a hole when we have 'clicked' a camera. This process is easily demonstrated by making a shoebox camera.

Remove the end from a shoebox and fix the lid firmly to the rest of the box with Sellotape.

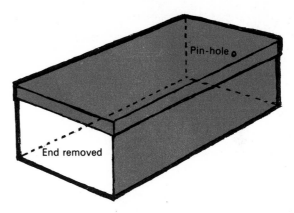

Make a small pin-hole at one end.

Construct a frame from wood, or card, that can be moved backward and forward in the box.

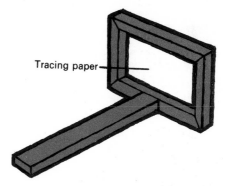

Cover the surface of this with tracing paper.

If this is held up to a window it should be possible to get an image of the window frame on the tracing paper by moving it to a suitable position in the box, where it is suitably shaded. Perhaps it helps if a dark cloth is draped over the head and the back of the box. Note that the picture is inverted.

Another model might be made from mapping tubes one of which fits inside the other.

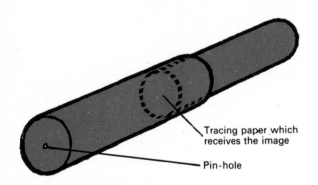

Tracing paper which receives the image

Pin-hole

It is worth looking at an empty box camera and seeing how it works. If the shutter is kept open it is possible to get a picture by putting tracing paper in the place normally occupied by the film. Many children might be interested in photography—a nice side-line to pursue.

## Holes and movement

Joseph Antoine Plateau, a Belgian, discovered a very intriguing effect produced by viewing pictures through holes which it is easy for children to duplicate. Older juniors with some perseverance might copy this invention.

Cut a circular disc about 25 cm in diameter, from card or hardboard and make a series of sawcuts around its outer edge.

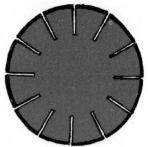

Drill a hole at the centre of the disc ready to receive a bent knitting needle, or a bolt, to act as a spindle on which to spin the disc.

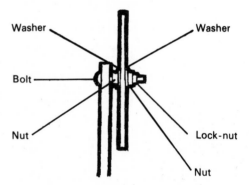

Washer          Washer

Bolt

Nut          Lock-nut

Nut

Cut a second disc, about 30 cm diameter from white card and remove the central portion of this so that it has a 1·5-cm overlap with the first disc.

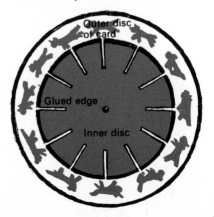

Outer disc of card

Glued edge

Inner disc

Draw a series of figures in movement around this. Children with artistic ability might draw a running dog. Firmly glue this disc to the smaller one as shown.

Hold the disc up to a mirror and spin it on its axis. View the figures through the slits and watch their apparent movement.

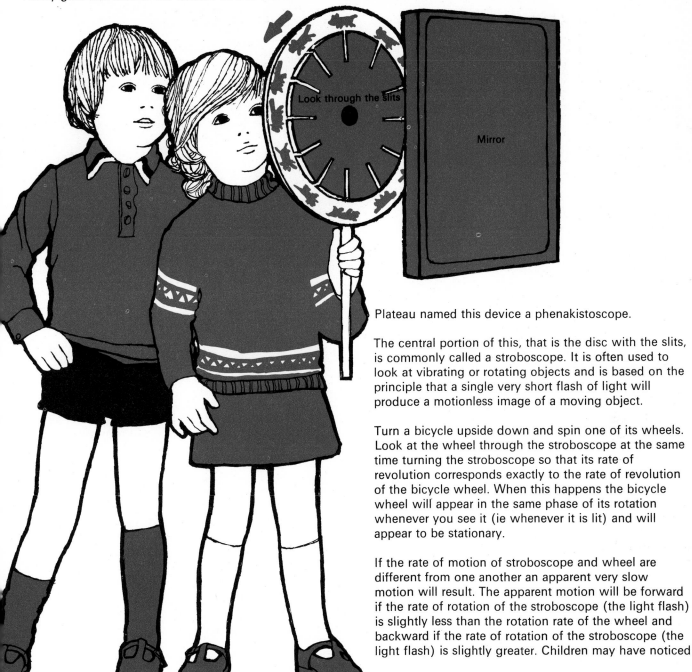

Look through the slits

Mirror

Plateau named this device a phenakistoscope.

The central portion of this, that is the disc with the slits, is commonly called a stroboscope. It is often used to look at vibrating or rotating objects and is based on the principle that a single very short flash of light will produce a motionless image of a moving object.

Turn a bicycle upside down and spin one of its wheels. Look at the wheel through the stroboscope at the same time turning the stroboscope so that its rate of revolution corresponds exactly to the rate of revolution of the bicycle wheel. When this happens the bicycle wheel will appear in the same phase of its rotation whenever you see it (ie whenever it is lit) and will appear to be stationary.

If the rate of motion of stroboscope and wheel are different from one another an apparent very slow motion will result. The apparent motion will be forward if the rate of rotation of the stroboscope (the light flash) is slightly less than the rotation rate of the wheel and backward if the rate of rotation of the stroboscope (the light flash) is slightly greater. Children may have noticed this latter effect on coach wheels in Western films. Such stroboscopic observation depends on our persistence of vision.

Try looking at other rotating objects such as a spinning top, a moving egg-beater, a grinding wheel and so on. Look also at the ripples on a bowl of water or the vibrating strings on a musical instrument.

There is a form of high-speed, single flash photography that is called strobe photography. No stroboscopic effect is really involved: what happens is that a series of exposures are taken on one film using successive flashes of light.

Stroboscopic observations depend on the ability of the brain to retain images for short periods of time—on persistence of vision. The classic way of demonstrating this phenomenon is by making up a disc to spin with a drawing of a bird on one side and a cage on the other.

Margot Fonteyn

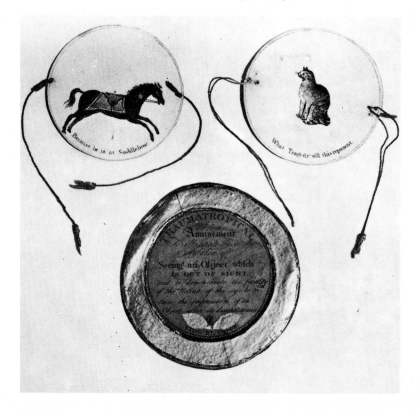

Thaumatrope discs

48

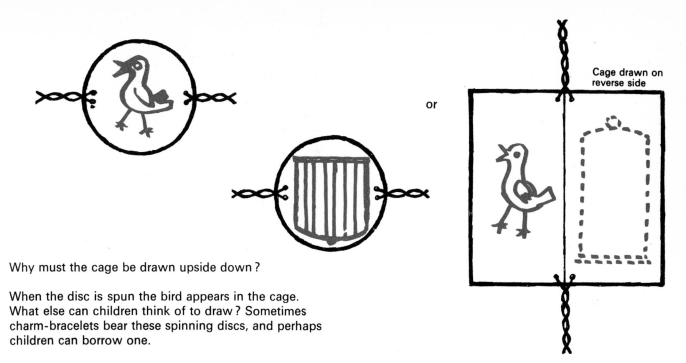

Why must the cage be drawn upside down?

When the disc is spun the bird appears in the cage. What else can children think of to draw? Sometimes charm-bracelets bear these spinning discs, and perhaps children can borrow one.

Another interesting way to demonstrate persistence of vision is to cut a piece of white card about 30 cm long and 6 cm wide. Mount a nut and bolt at the centre of this and fix the bolt firmly into the neck of a hand-drill.

Hold this up in front of a picture thrown from a slide projector, move to and fro until you find the correct distance to get the picture in focus. Now spin the hand-drill.

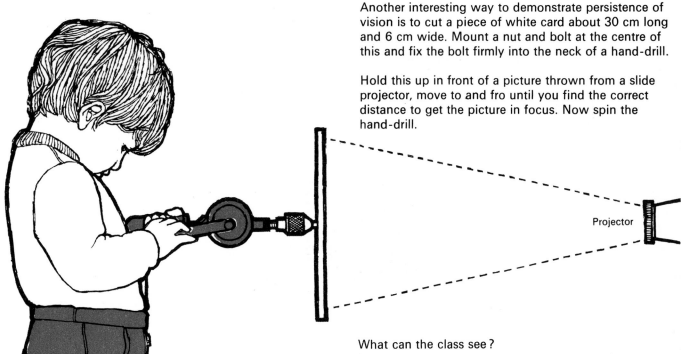

What can the class see?

In 1834 William George Horner, an English mathematician, produced a device that worked on the same principle as Joseph Plateau's phenakistoscope. He called it a zoetrope and it became a popular Victorian toy. Some older juniors might have enough dexterity to make one of their own.

Draw a circle of radius 8.75 cm (diameter 17.5 cm) on a piece of stout cardboard.

Cut this out and make a hole at the centre that will just take a steel knitting needle.

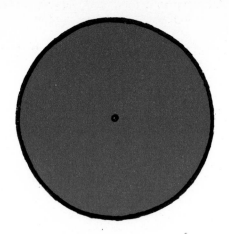

Cut a strip of black sugar paper 56 cm long and 14 cm wide. Make slits in this with a safety razor and a ruler, so that each slit is 5 cm long, 4 mm wide and 4 cm from its neighbour. The top of each slit should come 2.5 cm from the top of the paper.

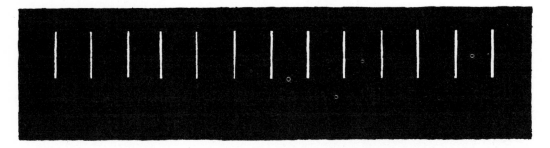

Stick a length of wide-band Sellotape carefully along the the lower edge of the strip with half of its length projecting over the edge of the black paper. Cut nicks all the way round.

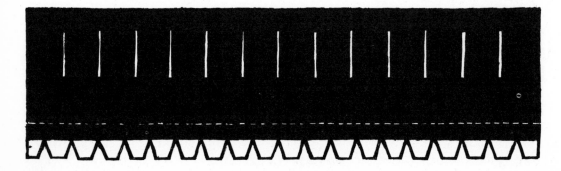

Cut a strip of metal (or strong card) about 12 cm long and 2 cm wide and bend it to form a bridge.

Knock a hole at each end with a hammer and nail.

Fix this, with paper fasteners, over the hole at the centre of the card circle.

Paper fasteners

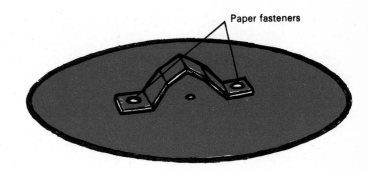

Run the strip of black paper with the slits around this card and firmly join the overlap with Sellotape. Make sure the card circle comes at the base of this drum so that the overlapping Sellotape can be stuck to it as shown.

View of base

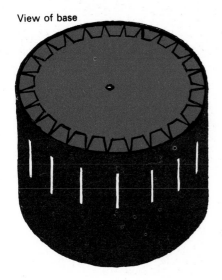

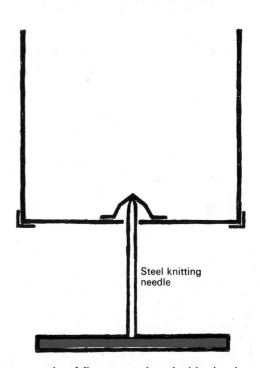

Steel knitting needle

Push the steel knitting needle up through the base of the drum so that the metal bridge rests on it. If possible mount the knitting needle in a wooden base block. Make sure the drum spins freely on the knitting needle.

Make up a strip of figures to place inside the drum. The spacing apart of the figures must match the spacing of the slits in the drum, ie they should be 4 cm apart and the strip itself about 5 cm high. There is an illustration on the next page.

Join aa to bb: cc to dd to make a continuous strip. The movement is always from right to left.

Place this strip inside the drum and set the drum revolving. Look through the slits. You will see the figures in apparent motion. This is because you only see one picture at a time as each slit comes opposite your eye, and this picture is then 'cut out' until the next slit comes into position. The effect of each picture persists in the eye until the next picture comes into view. You therefore get the effect of continuous movement.

It is sometimes easier to view the movement of the figures by holding a card with a slit in front of the revolving drum. Just one moving figure then appears in view.

Five phenakistoscope discs

# Holes and sorting

It is hard to beat hand and eye when it comes to sorting. One method used a lot in industry is by means of holes.

## Sieving

A place to begin might be by presenting children with a mixture of things, perhaps rice, wheat grains, sunflower seeds and sugar on a tray. Who can devise the most efficient and quickest way of separating the mixture?

Leave the problem with the children. Initially some may start picking out the larger seeds and find that this is time-consuming. Shaking the tray will bring the larger seeds to the top.

Sugar grains

Using a comb might help speed up the process.

What else will help speed up the process?

Someone will probably suggest a sieve. Try and form a large collection of sieves borrowed from home. Will these give a suitable range for your mixtures? Try sorting dry soil.

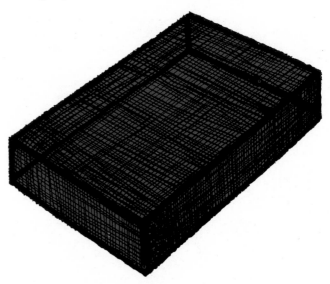

Sieves for some purposes can be constructed from wire framing covered in coarse mesh cloth.

Try making your own sorting box. The thin boxes that paper handkerchiefs come in are the best ones to use. What can you use to perforate the base of each box?

Large sewing needles, the point of a pair of compasses, knitting needles, bradawls, lino-cutting knives, might be useful. A set of cork borers are ideal. Will distributing the holes haphazardly or placing them to a pattern make a difference?

If you put marbles, rice, sugar and salt in the box marked 'A' where will they end up?

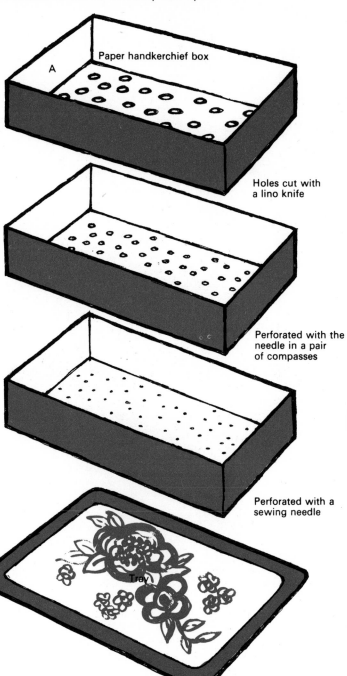

Paper handkerchief box

A

Holes cut with a lino knife

Perforated with the needle in a pair of compasses

Perforated with a sewing needle

Tray

With a hand-drill and a set of bits it is possible to get a finely graded set of boxes. You might even drill squares of hardboard and make a series of strong sorting trays.

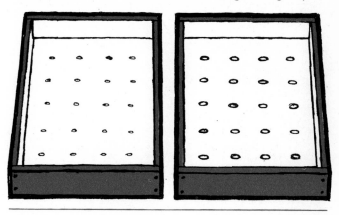

## Sorting machines

Why not have some fun and invent a number of sorting machines based on holes. Here are some suggestions.

Sort large marbles from small ones; dried peas from oak apples; round beads from plastic balls.

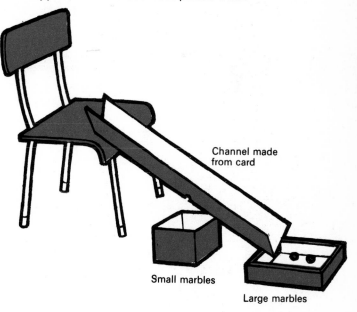

Channel made from card

Small marbles

Large marbles

If you take the idea further you might sort a series of
round objects as long as they differ in size.

Chalk box

Here is a simple but very effective method.

Round dowels

56

Try separating balls on their heights. Here is a device made up by some ten-year-olds.

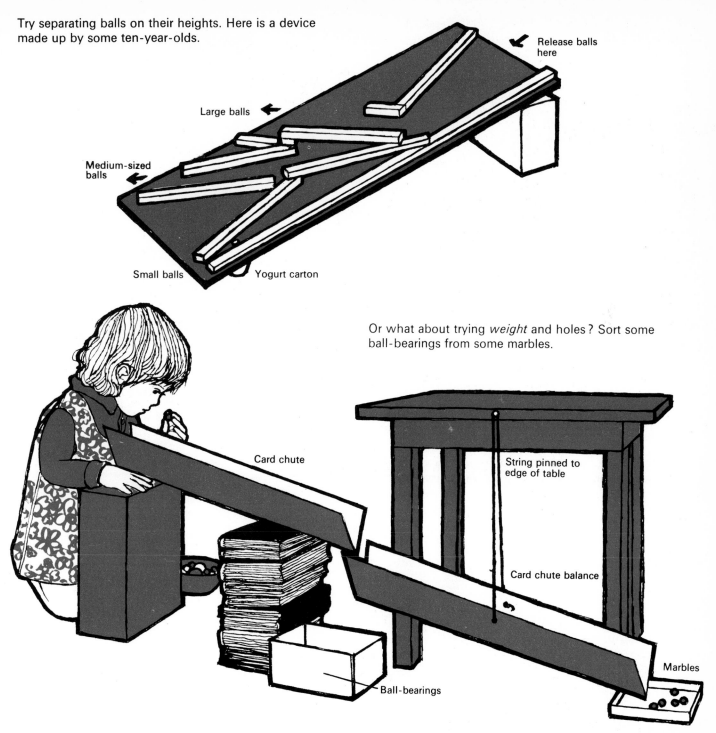

Release balls here

Large balls

Medium-sized balls

Small balls

Yogurt carton

Or what about trying *weight* and holes? Sort some ball-bearings from some marbles.

Card chute

String pinned to edge of table

Card chute balance

Ball-bearings

Marbles

You'll have to get the fulcrum of your balance just right so that it tips up and delivers the ball-bearings at one end but remains relatively still to send the marble down to the other.

What sorting devices can children come up with? It is hard to beat hand and eye when it comes to sorting.

Try and find all the places where man uses holes for sorting in this way.

How does a farmer sort his wheat grains from weed seeds? . . . potatoes into sizes? . . . peas into sizes?

What does it say on the sides of seed potato bags?

Where and for what does mother use sieves?

## Holes in fabrics

Here a start may be made by collecting a number of fabrics and garments.

Are there any holes in them?

Are they large or small holes?

Hold the fabrics up to the light.
The weave in a handkerchief is very easy to see

How are garments made?

What does a loom look like?

What are the warp and the weft?

Try weaving your own material using wool.

Try weaving with string, grasses, plantain flower stalks, raffia, reeds, sticks, large elastic bands, flattened drinking straws and so on.

What must you do to get the weave tighter together? Look at clothing and find out where there is a loose weave and where there is a tight weave.

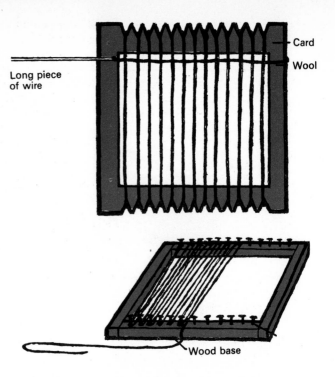

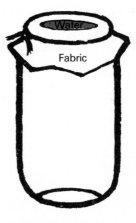

Take a range of fabrics and see how easy it is for water to pass through them. Try satin, cotton, nylon, a piece of gaberdine and so on.

Try a controlled experiment where you time the passage of a fixed amount of water through different materials.

Some fabrics will absorb water more quickly than others and the closeness of the weave will have an effect. Cotton usually takes up water easily because the spaces in the cloth are relatively large. Nylon, with a closer weave, is more reluctant to absorb water. Materials like gaberdine and canvas have such tiny holes that the surface tension of the water forms a 'skin' over them. Waterproof materials are also treated with chemicals which make the fibres of the cloth less absorbent—they are proofed.

Try water on gaberdine again, but this time add a drop of detergent.

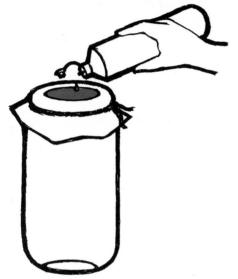

What happens?

Why do you set the washing-up bowl well away from the tent when camping? What happens if you touch the tent during rain?

Which materials would be best for making up into waterproof garments? Make a record of the sort of garments brought to school when it rains. How many are there of each garment? Make a block graph.

Is there any correlation between your findings about fabrics and the type of garment worn on rainy days?

Did you test rubber, plastic, nylon, cotton and so on?

## Holes in paper

Collect a range of papers, it's surprising how wide it can be. Get fine and coarse paper, glazed and unglazed, thick sheets and thin sheets. Try passing water through these. It may be best to line plastic funnels with the paper.

Fold it as shown.

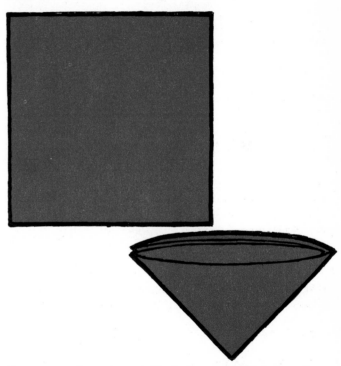

Pour water through each kind of paper. Which does it pass most easily through? What does this tell you about the nature of the paper? Time *fixed amounts* of water through each paper and graph your results.

One class treated this problem very meticulously. They measured the thicknesses of paper using a micrometer. Discussion eventually came round to why very large pieces were needed.

Holes in paper are intriguing and might interest some children in how paper is made.

## Paper tissues

How well do different paper tissues absorb water?
Collect a range of different brand-name paper tissues
and devise some methods of finding out.

You might fold each tissue to line a plastic funnel.

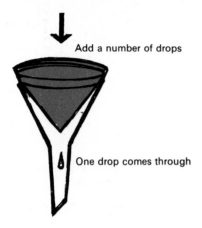

Add a number of drops

One drop comes through

How many drops of water must you add before one
drop comes through?

Try single, double, triple and double triple layers.

Another method might be to soak equal areas of tissue
in water for five seconds. Allow them to drip for ten
seconds then squeeze the remaining water into a small
jar.

The same sort of test can be carried out to compare the
absorption efficiencies of a range of sponges.

---

## Filtering and straining

---

Fabrics and paper can be used for filtering. Try
separating soil and water with the foot of a nylon
stocking, paper, a flour sieve, a colander lined with
muslin.

What else? What about things that dissolve in water,
can they be separated by filtering? Try salt. Try sugar.
How would you separate a mixture of sand and sugar?

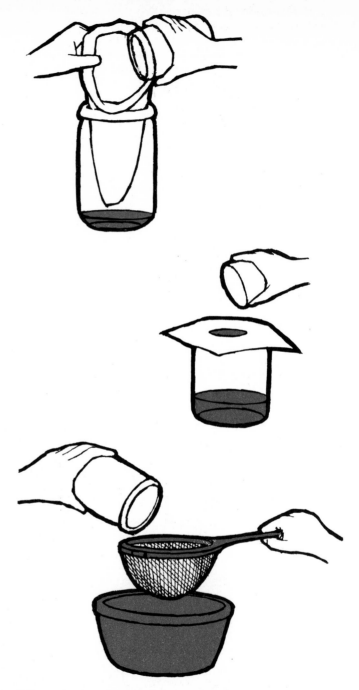

Where do we use this principle of separation?

# 1. Water purification

Children can try to purify dirty water.

Or make a more sophisticated version.

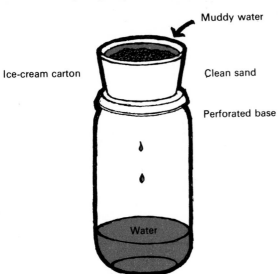

Muddy water

Ice-cream carton

Clean sand

Perforated base

Water

Fine silver sand

Sand

Clean gravel

Pebbles

Cotton wool

Who can devise the most efficient filter?

Slow sand filter bed.

## 2. Sewerage filtration

A city like Coventry deals with ninety million litres of waste water from its sewers each day. Large solid matter is screened off from this and grit is removed. Fine suspended solid matter is deposited as 'sludge' in sedimentation tanks. The most significant treatment is the breakdown of organic matter by bacteria in large circular tanks called percolating filters where the sewerage passes between small stones.

One of the troubles with school visits to industrial sites is that many of the working processes are obscured from view. This doesn't happen at the sewerage works, most things can be clearly seen.

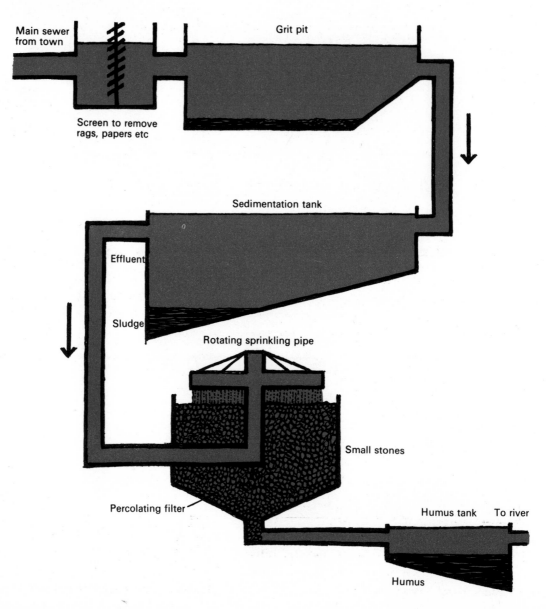

Main sewer from town

Grit pit

Screen to remove rags, papers etc

Sedimentation tank

Effluent

Sludge

Rotating sprinkling pipe

Small stones

Percolating filter

Humus tank    To river

Humus

## 3. Filtering out the fish

There are all kinds of fishing nets that are worth discussing. Take drift and trawl nets for example. The holes in a drift net are small and they are set down from *drifters* of the herring fleet to float just below the sea surface.

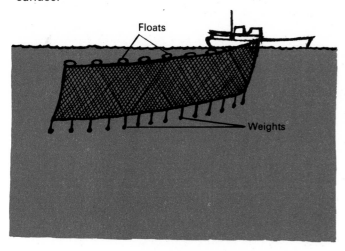

Trawlers have nets with a larger mesh and usually catch large fish such as cod. The net is drawn along the sea bottom.

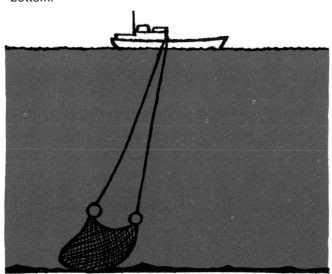

What other methods of fishing are there?

## 4. Spin-dryers

Here again is a form of filtering where water is separated from clothes by an outward throwing force. This force is easily demonstrated.

Put some lumps of Plasticine in the bottom of a plastic bucket and swing it round and round.

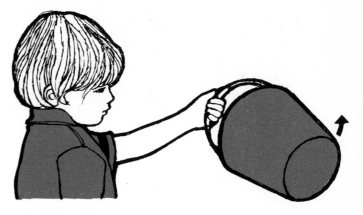

What happens to the Plasticine?

Do you have enough confidence to try some water in the bucket?

Get the children to make sketches of their spin-dryers at home. Can they improvise a spin-dryer? Here are some suggestions.

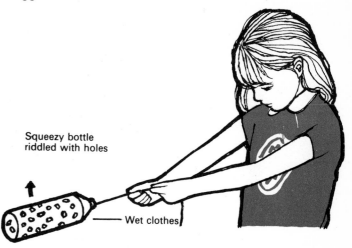

Squeezy bottle riddled with holes.

or

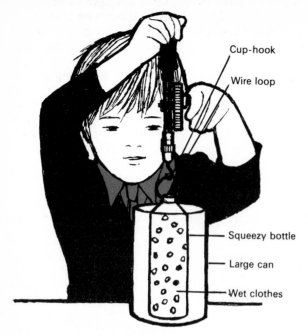

Cup-hook

Wire loop

Squeezy bottle

Large can

Wet clothes

The wet clothes fly outward but the water from them flies out even further into the outer can.

Particles are separated from liquids by a similar principle in a centrifuge.

Cream is also separated from milk in a dairy in this way.

## Soils

Of course, this principle of 'go and no go' sets problems for man. The farmer, for example, with heavy clay land has to put down drains because the soil structure is such that it is almost impermeable.

Begin by looking at the structure of soil with a lens. Take some soil from the school grounds and put a layer about 6 cm deep into a jam jar. Pour on the same volume of water and stir vigorously. Leave the jar for a day or so and look at the layers that form.

Where are the largest particles?

Where are the finest particles?

What floats on top of the water?

What does this tell you about the structure of soil?

Try and collect two samples of soil. One from heavy clay soil and one from sandy soil. (Many children need to be told that a sandy soil is a light loamy soil—it does not mean it is made of sand.) Put them in plastic bags and seal the tops until you are ready to use them. Spread each sample out on paper and pick it fairly clean of stones, twigs and so on and then weigh out the same amount of each. Reweigh each sample daily.

Which soil loses the most water?

Make a block graph to illustrate the daily loss of water.

What does this tell you about clay soil as compared to sandy soil?

Clay soil is made up of very small particles whereas a sandy soil has larger particles. The pore space between the particles therefore varies.

Take two jam jars, fill one with marbles and the other with beads.

Put water from a *graduated* container (see page 36) in each jar.

Marbles          Beads

Which one takes most water?

Which do you think will have the greatest total pore space, clay or sandy soil?

Take two plastic funnels. Put a cotton wool plug in the base of each and then fill one with clay and one with sandy soil.

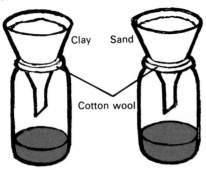

Saturate each with water.

When you are sure they are saturated pour equal amounts of water on each and find out how long it takes for water to drain through. Which soil drains most easily?

One of the reasons why farmers use lime on the land is because of its flocculating effect, ie it causes very small particles of soil to cling together. Repeat the experiment on drainage but this time compare a funnel packed with clay with a funnel packed with clay to which lime has been added. Which drains most quickly?

Find out how farmers drain their land. Try and find out about a mole drain. Look at the types of farming throughout the country. Can you suggest why dairy farming tends to predominate on heavy clay land?

Filtering out the fish

# Holes and natural objects

Nature abounds in holes

Life could not function without them, be it holes to let food in, a hole in an oak apple to let a wasp out or holes in plants that allow for gaseous diffusion.

## Holes in the head

A common expression about someone who does something silly is 'he's got a hole in the head'. In reality it would be unique if he hadn't.

Children can begin by examining their own heads for holes by looking and feeling. There's the mouth, the ears and the nostrils. Don't forget that the eyes are sunk into deep sockets in the skull. Feel the ridge of the cavity the eye is sunk into. Look closely, too, at the skin —use a magnifying glass if necessary. It is pitted with tiny pores leading from the sweat glands. Let's look at these aspects more closely.

### Mouths

Open and close the mouth slowly. Note the jaw's scissor-like action. Try and get hold of an animal's skull and have a look at the way the jaw hinges into the skull.

Provide plenty of mirrors for children to look at their teeth. Why does the mirror sometimes cloud over when they do this? Make some drawings.

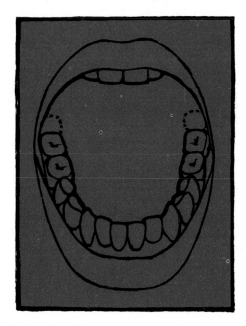

Human teeth as seen in a mirror

How many teeth do you have?

How many different kinds of teeth do you have in your mouth?

Count the teeth of ten children. What do you find about the number of teeth?

Make a picture with bits of sticky coloured paper.

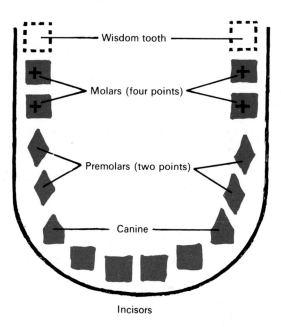

Incisors

Can you work out from their shape which teeth are for cutting? ... for biting? ... for grinding?

Have any been filled?

What causes decay of teeth?

Try and find out about the structure of teeth and the best ways of cleaning them.

Look at the teeth of school pets. If possible collect some jaws and skulls of different animals and work out what the different teeth are used for.

67

Try and look at the teeth of herbivores such as rabbits or sheep: carnivores such as dogs and cats and gnawing rodents such as mice, rats and guinea-pigs.

Teeth of herbivore (plant eater)

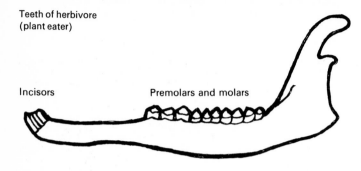

Incisors     Premolars and molars

Teeth of carnivore (meat eater)

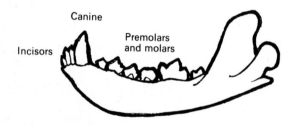

Canine

Premolars and molars

Incisors

Teeth of a rodent (a gnawer)

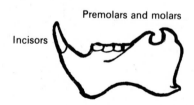

Premolars and molars

Incisors

Notice how in a rabbit's skull there is a wide gap between the biting teeth at the front and the grinding teeth. The rabbit's lips fold into this and help in pushing food back into the mouth.

The 'power' in a dog's jaw is very apparent and the scissor-like action of the teeth in slicing up meat can be clearly seen.

## More mouths

Look at the beaks of birds. Look at the multipurpose beak of a sparrow. What sorts of beaks are found in thrushes, robins and blackbirds? What do they feed on?

Make some drawings of bird beaks. Remember to consider birds of prey, with beaks for catching and tearing flesh; a heron, with its beak for spearing fish, and the curlew with its long narrow beak for probing into mud and sand to reach worms or molluscs. What others are there?

Look at goldfish in the aquarium. Fish in general have a wide gape for swallowing food whole.

Other animals worth considering are frogs, also with a wide gape, and a rear-hinged tongue which can be flicked out to catch flies. (A frog feeding on a worm is a never-to-be-forgotten sight) and snakes with jaws that can be completely disarticulated in order to swallow prey.

Again, caterpillar, beetle and snails' mouths are fascinating. Insect mouths are often just a series of paired jaws one behind the other. Watch a grasshopper chop up vegetation, or a caterpillar slice so neatly along the edge of a leaf.

Kentish glory larva feeding on a birch leaf

The radula, or file-like tongue, is easy to see in pond-snails and slugs. Watch a pond-snail scrape the algae off the side of an aquarium. Have a close look with a magnifying glass.

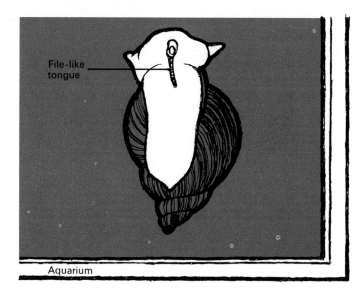

File-like tongue

Aquarium

Sea anemones and barnacles are available to some.

A barnacle

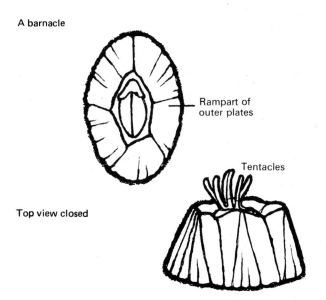

Rampart of outer plates

Top view closed

Tentacles

Side view open

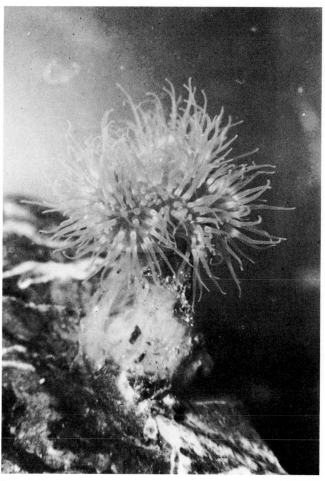

Sea anemone

**Holes made when feeding—a digression**
It's easy to see the effect our teeth have when we bite into a sandwich. What effect do other animals have when they feed?

School pets are easy to examine but look for signs left by wild animals as well. Gnawing by rodents is common. Squirrels, for example, crack nuts or gnaw at pine cones. Look, too, for signs of living branches having been attacked by them.

A hazel-nut attacked by a dormouse will show a neat rounded entry.

Look for pecking by birds, especially of fruit. Here is a picture of a bird pecking a hole in a milk-bottle top to get at the cream.

Aluminium milk bottle top

Why is this? Is it the colour of the top?

Is it reflection in the top?

What happens if you put out a bottle of water?

Do the old birds teach the young ones?

**Ears, eyes and noses**
Here are some more holes. Start by looking at ears in the class. What a fascinating variety of shapes there are! How many children have no lobes to their ears?

Look at the variety of ear shapes through the animal kingdom.

Collect pictures or make drawings to illustrate these.

In which animals is this external part of the ear important?

It is difficult to see external signs of the organs of hearing in many animals. Do frogs and birds have ears? Remember sounds are caused by vibrations. What do insects use to pick up vibrations?

Eyes vary enormously in position. In predators they tend to be at the front of the head whilst animals that are hunted have them more to the side in order to gain a wider field of vision. A fascinating thing to do on a zoo visit is to make a series of sketches showing the eye position of various animals. It's also worthwhile drawing in the size and shape of that other hole, the pupil. Where does this latter hole tend to be a narrow slit and where is it widely dilated? What does this tell you about the animal?

**Noses**
Look at nostrils too. Which of the school pets can move their nostrils? Where are the nostrils placed in an animal like a crocodile? Why is this? What about an elephant's nostrils?

**Holes and breathing—another digression**
Look for breathing holes. Start with the children. Take some breathing rates. How many breaths per minute when sitting quietly? . . . after jumping up and down? . . . after running round in the playground?

Great horned owl

Long eared bat

Find out who has the greatest lung capacity in the class. Set up a large container full of water (a plastic one is ideal), in a sink as shown and introduce a long length of rubber tubing or a hose pipe. Pinch your nose firmly and breathe out down the tubing.

Blow hard

How much water do you displace? Work out a way of calibrating the jar.

Don't forget to invert your scale before you stick it on!

How much air can you breathe out?

How much air can children in the class breathe out?

*Is there a link between chest size and air capacity of the lungs?*

Breathe out until the lungs are empty of air. Measure the chest.

Breathe in until the lungs are fully expanded. Measure the chest.

How much chest expansion do you have?

How much chest expansion does each of your friends have?

Is there a link between chest expansion and the amount of air expelled?

| Chest expansion (cm) | Amount of air expelled | Average |
|---|---|---|
| 2 | John   − − cm³<br>Sally   − − cm³<br>Wendy − − cm³ | |
| 3 | Peter<br>Roy<br>James<br>Martin | |
| 4 | Sheila<br>Lucy<br>Paul<br>Oliver | |
| 5 | Jane<br>Michael | |

Many children are interested in where the air goes to when they breathe in. Probably the only worthwhile way of considering this is to get some 'lights' from the butcher. If you tell him well in advance he'll probably let you have some sheep's lungs complete with windpipe and 'voice box'. It is easy to trace the path of the main tubes leading into the lungs from the windpipe if you use a sharp pointed knife. Notice how light and spongy the lungs are and how they will float in water. Squeeze a piece of lung under water and note what happens.

Look, too, at breathing holes of fish in the aquarium. Watch the opening and closing of the mouth and the gill covers. How many times a minute does this happen? How many times a minute if the fish are disturbed? It is worth looking at a fish, like a *herring*, in some detail. Get some from the fishmonger.

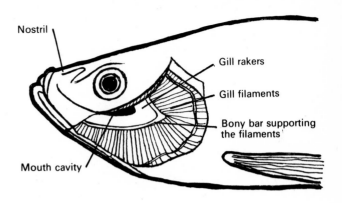

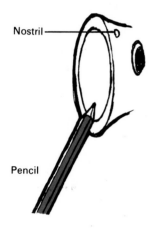

Note how wide the mouth is when you pull it open by pressing on the lower jaw.

Look for the nostrils at the top of the head.

Have the eyes any eye-lids? How wide a field of vision do you think a herring has? Look at the gill 'rakers' behind the tongue that help filter off food particles from the water.

Lift the gill cover and look at the gills. How many are there? Poke a pencil right through the mouth and see how it can come out over the gills.

Another water animal is the common pond snail. Watch it when it comes to the surface of an aquarium to take in air.

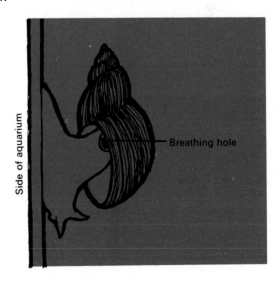

The hole leads to gills placed in a cavity under the shell.

Other water creatures such as mosquito larvae and water scorpions, which you may find when pond-dipping, have siphons (small tubes) which they poke up through the water surface to take in air.

Spiracles on insects and insect larvae such as caterpillars are also quite noticeable.

# Holes in the skeleton

Collect bones. Children can save bones from the meat and fish they eat at home; enlist the help of the school kitchen as well. Clean the bones by boiling them until it is easy to scrape the meat off. This is best done with the bones of mature animals since those of young animals tend to disintegrate when boiled.

Bones from chickens, rabbits and a shoulder or leg of lamb are usually easily obtained from home. Remember the butcher removes many large bones from meat before selling it and will probably help if you explain what you want.

Examine the bones for holes and cavities. In some such as the vertebrae of the backbone these holes are very obvious.

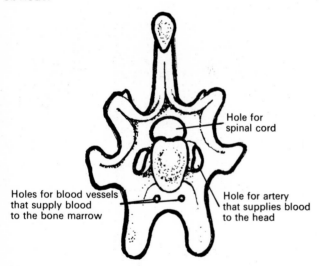

Hole for spinal cord

Holes for blood vessels that supply blood to the bone marrow

Hole for artery that supplies blood to the head

Similarly in the skull there are many holes and cavities: where the ears entered, where the eyes once were, where the nasal cavities are and where nerves and blood vessels passed. All these are easily seen in any animal's skull. Note too the curled up scroll bones in the nasal cavity. These were once lined with skin and hairs and helped filter dust particles from the air. The skull, of course, has a large cavity which contains and protects the brain.

Work out the skull capacity of any animal skulls you can get. Block up all holes leading into the skull with clay or Plasticine but leave the main hole where the spinal cord enters. Pour salt in until the cavity is full. You'll probably find some holes you missed plugging.

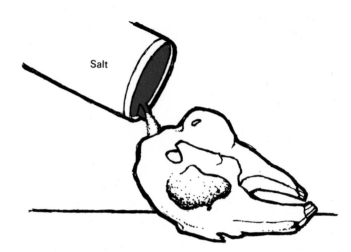

Salt

What is the capacity of your animal skull? That of man is about 1450 cm$^3$. One school tried finding the skull capacity with sand. They had earlier filled the skull with water (to check if all exits were closed) and found that the damp sand clung to the inside of the cavity. The skull capacity was therefore worked out in terms of dried peas. Their results are below:

| | |
|---|---|
| Human skull | 3000 dried peas |
| Cow | 1400 dried peas |
| Sheep | 250 dried peas |
| Pig | 220 dried peas |
| Dog | 200 dried peas |
| Fox | 95 dried peas |
| Cat | 80 dried peas |
| Rabbit | 60 dried peas |

Note that the skull is made of separate bones joined by sutures. In a young baby's first year of life several skull bones are unconnected leaving a hole, the soft spot of the skull. Those children in the class with baby brothers or sisters may know this and the care a mother takes with the baby's head.

Most children will also note the holes where some bones

join others and the most observant may note the tiny holes that are found on a bone's surface. Look at a ball and socket joint and a hinge joint.

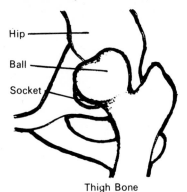

Hip

Ball

Socket

Thigh Bone

Ball and socket joint

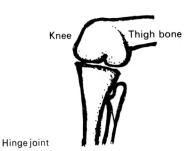

Knee        Thigh bone

Hinge joint

It is obvious why each is called by these terms. Try and think of other ball and socket joints—in a car wing mirror, or a shower nozzle, or 'poppet' beads.

Try articulating two bones from the backbone together. Notice that there are little cavities where they fit (although for ease of movement there should be a pad of cartilage which is probably missing).

Thread a drinking straw on string.

Cut it into three pieces and rethread these.

Now cut it into smaller pieces.

Does the articulation of the drinking straw pieces help you understand the need for a highly jointed backbone?

Try walking around with joints held stiff. Or better still strap up the joints with pieces of timber and note the effect this has on movement.

Such work might lead to a greater consideration of the skeleton and its function. A very few children may want to try piecing a whole skeleton together. This is difficult but it is certainly possible to put bits of limbs or the backbone together.

Don't forget there are cavities in bones. Cut a large fresh bone in half with a hacksaw and look at the hollow central part filled with soft marrow that manufactures blood. If you cut a bird wing bone you won't find this marrow, only air cavities which make for lightness. What about skeletons of other animals?

What was once in these holes or cavities?

Do snails, crabs, insects, frogs and fish have skeletons?

Where are the holes and cavities in these?

What function do they have?

Snails' shells are easy to collect. Remember they live in water as well as on land. Don't forget to look in crevices on tree trunks. If you collect them from different places you'll find they are choosy about where to lie. You won't, for example, find any in pine woods.

The dead body of a snail can be removed with a bent pin. Mount a collection on card.

Stags horn coral

Freshwater sponge

76

# Holes to live in

Hermit crab

Most animals like somewhere to hide away. They may, as with a snail, have a hard external covering that protects them, they may dig a hole or a burrow or they may live in some cavity or den. Collect pictures showing where animals live.

## Burrowers
### Worms
Begin by looking for that common burrower—the worm. Most children know that they 'eat' their way through the soil. In reality they push their way through where the soil particles are loose and eat their way where the soil is firmer. Just try digging with a trowel in a flower-bed and in ground that has been down to grass for some time to see the difference.

Now dig a hole in the ground with a spade. Refill it. Can you get all the earth back in? Inevitably there is some soil over. The loosening of the soil particles causes them to take up a greater volume. Worms when burrowing cope with this by making worm casts on the soil surface. Look for these and note how they are made of very fine particles.

You'll probably find some worms when you are digging. They have two double rows of bristles on their undersurface which together with muscular contractions of the body help them move. Put a worm on to some brown paper. Can you hear the bristles scratching? If you see a worm emerging from its burrow move very quickly and grab it. Pull steadily but *slowly* or it will break. You'll be surprised how strong a pull it gives as it digs its bristles into the ground.

Inevitably children will want to find out more about worms. How many segments do they have? How do they reproduce? How do they respond to stimuli and so on?

Does a worm respond to light when it emerges from the hole at the end of its burrow? Put a worm in a shoebox and carry it to a darkened part of the classroom, a store-room is ideal. Shine the light from a torch on to it. Bring the torch beam *very near* to the front end of the earthworm.

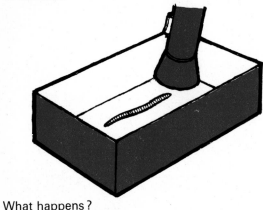

What happens?

## Lugworms

These are favourites with fishermen and well worth looking for on any school visit to a sandy shore. A lugworm lives in a U-shaped tunnel on sandy beaches and lines the walls with a cement-like secretion to prevent them collapsing inward.

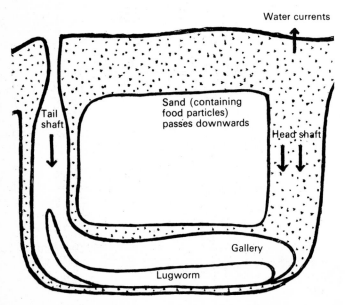

The worm maintains a current of water through the tube and extracts oxygen from this for breathing. Sand containing food material passes down the head shaft. The tail is poked out through the tail shaft periodically and the familiar 'casts' left on the sand surface.

## Razor shells

This is another burrowing marine animal which is quite common. Some children may have shells they can bring to school.

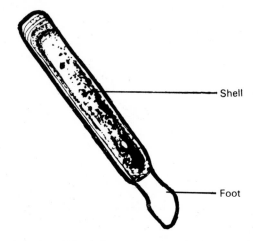

The foot is pushed down into the sand and its tip swells forming a ball-like anchor. The rest of the foot then contracts pulling the animal into the ground.

These movements, repeated rapidly, enable the animal to burrow very quickly into the ground, as anyone who has dug for them will know.

The razor shell belongs to a group of animals called bivalve molluscs. These are animals with two overlapping shells, which are relatives of the snail. The notorious common shipworm, *Teredo norvegica*, which plays havoc with wooden-hulled ships, is one of these. There are even rock-boring molluscs some of which penetrate rocks by mechanical action. The piddock, for example, has rows of spires near its front edge which by a twisting motion of the animal rasp away a hole in the rock.

It is worth looking at some common bivalves whilst on this topic. Some children in the class can usually rustle up some shells collected at the seaside. Cockles and mussels are common bivalves. Examine these for holes.

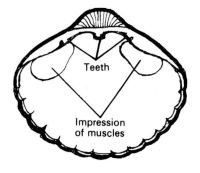

Teeth

Impression
of muscles

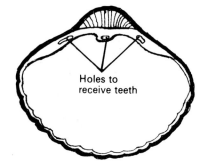

Holes to
receive teeth

Note how the hinge between the two shells contains teeth on one shell which lock into holes in the other. Look also for the marks left by the muscles which held the two valves together.

## Other holes to live in

Consider those animals that create their own homes. Ants are a good example and can be kept in a formicarium (see *Minibeasts*). If you find a few ants it's easy to set them up in a temporary home, a large jam jar will do.

Three-quarters fill this with loamy soil, put in the ants and cover the top with muslin.

Feed the ants on sugar lumps and pieces of apple, and put in some rose leaves bearing aphids.

Cover the sides with black paper.

The galleries made by the ants should be visible in about a week.

Look, too, at other dwellings, a wasp's nest, a swallow's nest or a rabbit's burrow. Consider a badger's set. It might even be possible for you to find some mole-hills. Can you tell which way the runs go underground? Cut some of the hills away to find the mole's tunnel.

## Other holes
Inevitably in considering such a topic as this children are going to bring up for discussion holes or openings in animals that are used for excretion, egestion and reproduction. Questions about such openings will arise naturally and can generally be dealt with by frank discussion.

Nest of common wasp

# Holes in plants

Where are the holes in plants? They are usually very small, often not even visible to the naked eye. Some worth examining are those in the leaf that allow diffusion of gases and the internal 'holes' that are sometimes visible if you cut across a stem.

## Holes in leaves

Firmly tie a polythene bag over the end of a leafy tree branch and leave it for a morning to collect some of the water given off. Is the water given off from holes in the leaf or from holes in the twig? One way of finding an answer might be to cover a denuded twig with a polythene bag and note the effect.

Does the upper or lower surface of a leaf give off most water? Perhaps putting Vaseline on different leaf surfaces would help give an answer here.

## Holes in stems

Cut across stems. Which are woody and which are not? Where do you find large cells and where are cells very small? Which stems are hollow?

Robert Hooke was one of the first people to investigate the 'holes' in a piece of cork. What can children find out about him?

Where does water rise in a plant stem? Wash the soil very gently away from the roots of a weed such as groundsel and stand it in a jam jar of coloured water. Look at the flowers after a day and cut across the stem. The groups of cells that carry water up the stem will show up as coloured dots. Try other plants.

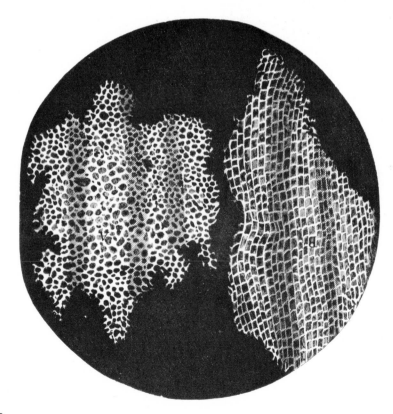

Cork cells drawn by Robert Hooke

# Objectives for children learning science
## Guide lines to keep in mind

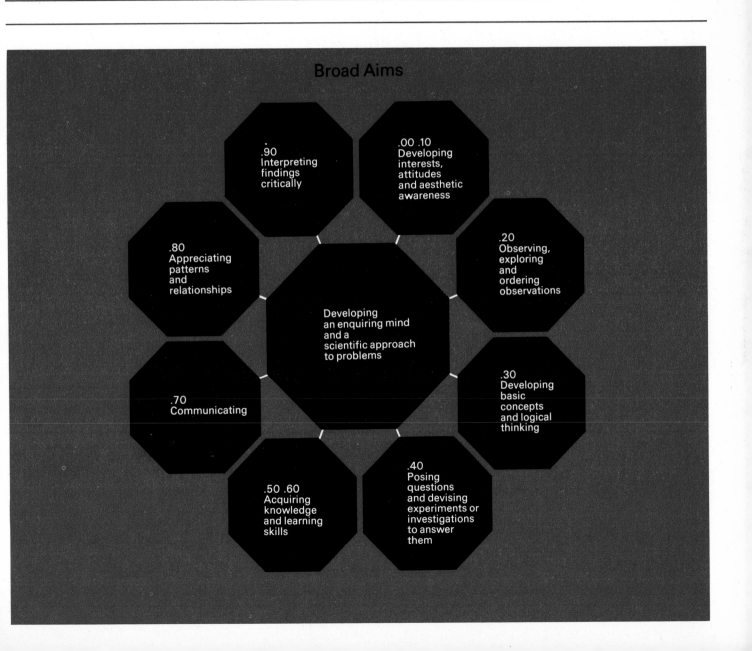

Broad Aims

.90 Interpreting findings critically

.00 .10 Developing interests, attitudes and aesthetic awareness

.80 Appreciating patterns and relationships

.20 Observing, exploring and ordering observations

Developing an enquiring mind and a scientific approach to problems

.70 Communicating

.30 Developing basic concepts and logical thinking

.50 .60 Acquiring knowledge and learning skills

.40 Posing questions and devising experiments or investigations to answer them

# What we mean by Stage 1, Stage 2 and Stage 3

# Attitudes, interests and aesthetic awareness

## Stage 1
Transition from intuition to concrete operations. Infants generally.

The characteristics of thought among infant children differ in important respects from those of children over the age of about seven years. Infant thought has been described as 'intuitive' by Piaget; it is closely associated with physical action and is dominated by immediate observation. Generally, the infant is not able to think about or imagine the consequences of an action unless he has actually carried it out, nor is he yet likely to draw logical conclusions from his experiences. At this early stage the objectives are those concerned with active exploration of the immediate environment and the development of ability to discuss and communicate effectively: they relate to the kind of activities that are appropriate to these very young children, and which form an introduction to ways of exploring and of ordering observations.

1.01 Willingness to ask questions
1.02 Willingness to handle both living and non-living material.
1.03 Sensitivity to the need for giving proper care to living things.
1.04 Enjoyment in using all the senses for exploring and discriminating.
1.05 Willingness to collect material for observation or investigation.

---

Concrete operations. Early stage.

In this Stage, children are developing the ability to manipulate things mentally. At first this ability is limited to objects and materials that can be manipulated concretely, and even then only in a restricted way. The objectives here are concerned with developing these mental operations through exploration of concrete objects and materials—that is to say, objects and materials which, as physical things, have meaning for the child. Since older children, and even adults prefer an introduction to new ideas and problems through concrete example and physical exploration, these objectives are suitable for all children, whatever their age, who are being introduced to certain science activities for the first time.

1.06 Desire to find out things for oneself.
1.07 Willing participation in group work.
1.08 Willing compliance with safety regulations in handling tools and equipment.
1.09 Appreciation of the need to learn the meaning of new words and to use them correctly.

## Stage 2
Concrete operations. Later stage.

In this Stage, a continuation of what Piaget calls the stage of concrete operations, the mental manipulations are becoming more varied and powerful. The developing ability to handle variables—for example, in dealing with multiple classification—means that problems can be solved in more ordered and quantitative ways than was previously possible. The objectives begin to be more specific to the exploration of the scientific aspects of the environment rather than to general experience, as previously. These objectives are developments of those of Stage 1 and depend on them for a foundation. They are those thought of as being appropriate for all children who have progressed from Stage 1 and not merely for nine- to eleven-year-olds.

2.01 Willingness to co-operate with others in science activities.
2.02 Willingness to observe objectively.
2.03 Appreciation of the reasons for safety regulations.
2.04 Enjoyment in examining ambiguity in the use of words.
2.05 Interest in choosing suitable means of expressing results and observations.
2.06 Willingness to assume responsibility for the proper care of living things.
2.07 Willingness to examine critically the results of their own and others' work.
2.08 Preference for putting ideas to test before accepting or rejecting them.
2.09 Appreciation that approximate methods of comparison may be more appropriate than careful measurements.

## Stage 3
Transition to stage of abstract thinking.

This is the Stage in which, for some children, the ability to think about abstractions is developing. When this development is complete their thought is capable of dealing with the possible and hypothetical, and is not tied to the concrete and to the here and now. It may take place between eleven and thirteen for some able children, for some children it may happen later, and for others it may never occur. The objectives of this stage are ones which involve development of ability to use hypothetical reasoning and to separate and combine variables in a systematic way. They are appropriate to those who have achieved most of the Stage 2 objectives and who now show signs of ability to manipulate mentally ideas and propositions.

3.01 Acceptance of responsibility for their own and others' safety in experiments.
3.02 Preference for using words correctly.
3.03 Commitment to the idea of physical cause and effect.
3.04 Recognition of the need to standardise measurements.
3.05 Willingness to examine evidence critically.
3.06 Willingness to consider beforehand the usefulness of the results from a possible experiment.
3.07 Preference for choosing the most appropriate means of expressing results or observations.
3.08 Recognition of the need to acquire new skills.
3.09 Willingness to consider the role of science in everyday life.

## Attitudes, interests and aesthetic awareness

### .00/.10

## Observing, exploring and ordering observations

### .20

1.21 Appreciation of the variety of living things and materials in the environment.
1.22 Awareness of changes which take place as time passes.
1.23 Recognition of common shapes—square, circle, triangle.
1.24 Recognition of regularity in patterns.
1.25 Ability to group things consistently according to chosen or given criteria.

---

1.11 Awareness that there are various ways of testing out ideas and making observations.
1.12 Interest in comparing and classifying living or non-living things.
1.13 Enjoyment in comparing measurements with estimates.
1.14 Awareness that there are various ways of expressing results and observations.
1.15 Willingness to wait and to keep records in order to observe change in things.
1.16 Enjoyment in exploring the variety of living things in the environment.
1.17 Interest in discussing and comparing the aesthetic qualities of materials.

1.26 Awareness of the structure and form of living things.
1.27 Awareness of change of living things and non-living materials.
1.28 Recognition of the action of force
1.29 Ability to group living and non-living things by observable attributes.
1.29a Ability to distinguish regularity in events and motion.

2.11 Enjoyment in developing methods for solving problems or testing ideas.
2.12 Appreciation of the part that aesthetic qualities of materials play in determining their use.
2.13 Interest in the way discoveries were made in the past.

2.21 Awareness of internal structure in living and non-living things.
2.22 Ability to construct and use keys for identification.
2.23 Recognition of similar and congruent shapes.
2.24 Awareness of symmetry in shapes and structures.
2.25 Ability to classify living things and non-living materials in different ways.
2.26 Ability to visualise objects from different angles and the shape of cross-sections.

3.11 Appreciation of the main principles in the care of living things.
3.12 Willingness to extend methods used in science activities to other fields of experience.

3.21 Appreciation that classification criteria are arbitrary.
3.22 Ability to distinguish observations which are relevant to the solution of a problem from those which are not.
3.23 Ability to estimate the order of magnitude of physical quantities.

| Developing basic concepts and logical thinking | Posing questions and devising experiments or investigations to answer them |
|---|---|
| .30 | .40 |

**Stage 1**
Transition from intuition to concrete operations. Infants generally.

*1.31* Awareness of the meaning of words which describe various types of quantity.
*1.32* Appreciation that things which are different may have features in common.

*1.41* Ability to find answers to simple problems by investigation.
*1.42* Ability to make comparisons in terms of one property or variable.

- - - - - - - - - - - - - - - - - - - - - - - - - - - - - - - -

Concrete operations. Early stage.

*1.33* Ability to predict the effect of certain changes through observation of similar changes.
*1.34* Formation of the notions of the horizontal and the vertical.
*1.35* Development of concepts of conservation of length and substance.
*1.36* Awareness of the meaning of speed and of its relation to distance covered.

*1.43* Appreciation of the need for measurement.
*1.44* Awareness that more than one variable may be involved in a particular change.

**Stage 2**
Concrete operations. Later stage.

*2.31* Appreciation of measurement as division into regular parts and repeated comparison with a unit.
*2.32* Appreciation that comparisons can be made indirectly by use of an intermediary.
*2.33* Development of concepts of conservation of weight, area and volume.
*2.34* Appreciation of weight as a downward force.
*2.35* Understanding of the speed, time, distance relation.

*2.41* Ability to frame questions likely to be answered through investigations.
*2.42* Ability to investigate variables and to discover effective ones.
*2.43* Appreciation of the need to control variables and use controls in investigations.
*2.44* Ability to choose and use either arbitrary or standard units of measurement as appropriate.
*2.45* Ability to select a suitable degree of approximation and work to it.
*2.46* Ability to use representational models for investigating problems or relationships.

**Stage 3**
Transition to stage of abstract thinking.

*3.31* Familiarity with relationships involving velocity, distance, time, acceleration.
*3.32* Ability to separate, exclude or combine variables in approaching problems.
*3.33* Ability to formulate hypotheses not dependent upon direct observation.
*3.34* Ability to extend reasoning beyond the actual to the possible.
*3.35* Ability to distinguish a logically sound proof from others less sound.

*3.41* Attempting to identify the essential steps in approaching a problem scientifically.
*3.42* Ability to design experiments with effective controls for testing hypotheses.
*3.43* Ability to visualise a hypothetical situation as a useful simplification of actual observations.
*3.44* Ability to construct scale models for investigation and to appreciate implications of changing the scale.

*1.51*  Ability to discriminate between different materials.
*1.52*  Awareness of the characteristics of living things.
*1.53*  Awareness of properties which materials can have.
*1.54*  Ability to use displayed reference material for identifying living and non-living things.

---

*1.55*  Familiarity with sources of sound.
*1.56*  Awareness of sources of heat, light and electricity.
*1.57*  Knowledge that change can be produced in common substances.
*1.58*  Appreciation that ability to move or cause movement requires energy.
*1.59*  Knowledge of differences in properties between and within common groups of materials.

*1.61*  Appreciation of man's use of other living things and their products.
*1.62*  Awareness that man's way of life has changed through the ages.
*1.63*  Skill in manipulating tools and materials.
*1.64*  Development of techniques for handling living things correctly.
*1.65*  Ability to use books for supplementing ideas or information.

*2.51*  Knowledge of conditions which promote changes in living things and non-living materials.
*2.52*  Familiarity with a wide range of forces and of ways in which they can be changed.
*2.53*  Knowledge of sources and simple properties of common forms of energy.
*2.54*  Knowledge of the origins of common materials.
*2.55*  Awareness of some discoveries and inventions by famous scientists.
*2.56*  Knowledge of ways to investigate and measure properties of living things and non-living materials.
*2.57*  Awareness of changes in the design of measuring instruments and tools during man's history.
*2.58*  Skill in devising and constructing simple apparatus.
*2.59*  Ability to select relevant information from books or other reference material.

*3.51*  Knowledge that chemical change results from interaction.
*3.52*  Knowledge that energy can be stored and converted in various ways.
*3.53*  Awareness of the universal nature of gravity.
*3.54*  Knowledge of the main constituents and variations in the composition of soil and of the earth.
*3.55*  Knowledge that properties of matter can be explained by reference to its particulate nature.
*3.56*  Knowledge of certain properties of heat, light, sound, electrical, mechanical and chemical energy.
*3.57*  Knowledge of a wide range of living organisms.
*3.58*  Development of the concept of an internal environment.
*3.59*  Knowledge of the nature and variations in basic life processes.

*3.61*  Appreciation of levels of organisation in living things.
*3.62*  Appreciation of the significance of the work and ideas of some famous scientists.
*3.63*  Ability to apply relevant knowledge without help of contextual cues.
*3.64*  Ability to use scientific equipment and instruments for extending the range of human senses.

| | Communicating | Appreciating patterns and relationships |
|---|---|---|
| | **.70** | **.80** |
| **Stage 1**<br>Transition from intuition to concrete operations. Infants generally. | *1.71* Ability to use new words appropriately.<br>*1.72* Ability to record events in their sequences.<br>*1.73* Ability to discuss and record impressions of living and non-living things in the environment.<br>*1.74* Ability to use representational symbols for recording information on charts or block graphs. | *1.81* Awareness of cause-effect relationships. |
| Concrete operations. Early stage. | *1.75* Ability to tabulate information and use tables.<br>*1.76* Familiarity with names of living things and non-living materials.<br>*1.77* Ability to record impressions by making models, painting or drawing. | *1.82* Development of a concept of environment.<br>*1.83* Formation of a broad idea of variation in living things.<br>*1.84* Awareness of seasonal changes in living things.<br>*1.85* Awareness of differences in physical conditions between different parts of the Earth. |
| **Stage 2**<br>Concrete operations. Later stage. | *2.71* Ability to use non-representational symbols in plans, charts, etc.<br>*2.72* Ability to interpret observations in terms of trends and rates of change.<br>*2.73* Ability to use histograms and other simple graphical forms for communicating data.<br>*2.74* Ability to construct models as a means of recording observations. | *2.81* Awareness of sequences of change in natural phenomena.<br>*2.82* Awareness of structure-function relationship in parts of living things.<br>*2.83* Appreciation of interdependence among living things.<br>*2.84* Awareness of the impact of man's activities on other living things.<br>*2.85* Awareness of the changes in the physical environment brought about by man's activity.<br>*2.86* Appreciation of the relationships of parts and wholes. |
| **Stage 3**<br>Transition to stage of abstract thinking. | *3.71* Ability to select the graphical form most appropriate to the information being recorded.<br>*3.72* Ability to use three-dimensional models or graphs for recording results.<br>*3.73* Ability to deduce information from graphs: from gradient, area, intercept.<br>*3.74* Ability to use analogies to explain scientific ideas and theories. | *3.81* Recognition that the ratio of volume to surface area is significant.<br>*3.82* Appreciation of the scale of the universe.<br>*3.83* Understanding of the nature and significance of changes in living and non-living things.<br>*3.84* Recognition that energy has many forms and is conserved when it is changed from one form to another.<br>*3.85* Recognition of man's impact on living things— conservation, change, control.<br>*3.86* Appreciation of the social implications of man's changing use of materials, historical and contemporary.<br>*3.87* Appreciation of the social implications of research in science.<br>*3.88* Appreciation of the role of science in the changing pattern of provision for human needs. |

# Interpreting findings critically

## .90

*1.91* Awareness that the apparent size, shape and relationships of things depend on the position of the observer.

---

*1.92* Appreciation that properties of materials influence their use.

---

*2.91* Appreciation of adaptation to environment.
*2.92* Appreciation of how the form and structure of materials relate to their function and properties.
*2.93* Awareness that many factors need to be considered when choosing a material for a particular use.
*2.94* Recognition of the role of chance in making measurements and experiments.

These Stages we have chosen conform to modern ideas about children's learning. They conveniently describe for us the mental development of children between the ages of five and thirteen years, but it must be remembered that ALTHOUGH CHILDREN GO THROUGH THESE STAGES IN THE SAME ORDER THEY DO NOT GO THROUGH THEM AT THE SAME RATES.
SOME children achieve the later Stages at an early age.
SOME loiter in the early Stages for quite a time.
SOME never have the mental ability to develop to the later Stages.
ALL appear to be ragged in their movement from one Stage to another.
Our Stages, then, are not tied to chronological age, so in any one class of children there will be, almost certainly, some children at differing Stages of mental development.

---

*3.91* Ability to draw from observations conclusions that are unbiased by preconception.
*3.92* Willingness to accept factual evidence despite perceptual contradictions.
*3.93* Awareness that the degree of accuracy of measurements has to be taken into account when results are interpreted.
*3.94* Awareness that unstated assumptions can affect conclusions drawn from argument or experimental results.
*3.95* Appreciation of the need to integrate findings into a simplifying generalisation.
*3.96* Willingness to check that conclusions are consistent with further evidence.

# Index